THE DOMESTIC DOG

THE DOMESTIC DOG

An Introduction to its History

by

BRIAN VESEY-FITZGERALD

Routledge and Kegan Paul
LONDON

First published 1957
by Routledge & Kegan Paul Limited
Broadway House, Carter Lane, E.C.4.
Printed in Great Britain by
Hazell Watson and Viney Ltd.,
Aylesbury and London

LIST OF ILLUSTRATIONS

I

THE NATURAL HISTORY OF THE DOG

THE dogs, the wolves and their relatives belong to a family of carnivorous mammals known as the *Canidæ*. This family includes (in addition to the dogs and the wolves) the coyotes, the dingo and the jackals; the numerous northern foxes; the fennec of North Africa and the deserts of Sinai and Arabia; the African Hunting-dog; the Indian Wild Dog or Dhole; the Japanese Raccoon-dog; the various wild dogs and foxes of South America; and the South American Bush-dog. In addition to these modern members of the family, there is a large number of extinct canids, the majority of which did not resemble modern dogs at all, but a few of which would immediately be recognised as dogs to-day even by the least observant.

In order to achieve some understanding of the evolution of the dog family, we have to go back a matter of some forty million years in geological history to the transition from the Eocene to the Oligocene period. Mammals then were comparatively new upon earth, and none of them was large. Horses then were the size of small sheep and had three toes upon each foot; camels resembled small hornless antelopes rather than camels, and the rhinoceros was small and horse-like, hornless and probably harmless. And there was also, at that time, a small carnivorous mammal known as *Miacis*. *Miacis* was an arboreal animal with a long body and relatively short legs, and with a tail as long as its body. It was about the size of a polecat. Some of the modern African and Indian civets closely resemble it in appearance and in their arboreal habits. *Miacis* was the primitive ancestor of the dogs and bears.

From *Miacis* stock there developed, during the Oligocene period, two larger animals, *Daphœnus* and *Cynodictis*. *Daphœnus* was about the size of the modern coyote, but longer-bodied and with relatively short legs, a massive skull, and a very long and heavy tail. As time passed, these animals became larger and larger, until, some ten million years ago, they attained positively gigantic proportions. Some then became extinct, but others branched off on a line of evolution which involved a great increase in weight and a change from a running gait to a slow and lumbering walk. Thus arose the first bears.

Cynodictis was a much smaller and more slender animal. It kept the long body and the short legs of its ancestor; indeed, it probably resembled *Miacis* closely in everything but size, for it retained the arboreal habits to a very large extent, and had retractile claws like those of a cat. During the Miocene period, *Cynodictis* gave rise to two distinct groups of long-legged animals, the first true canids. One of these, *Temnocyon*, the earlier of the two, was the ancestor of the line whose modern representatives are the hunting-dogs of Africa and India and the bush-dog of South America. The other, *Cynodesmus*, gave rise to two branches, one of which was destined to become extinct. The other was headed by *Tomarctus*, which was the ancestor of the line among whose modern representatives is the domestic dog.

Of the descendants of *Temnocyon*, the best known is probably the African Hunting-dog (*Lycaon pictus*). The range of the hunting-dog comprises the greater part of Africa from the Cape to the Sudan, and naturalists have recognised several local races. Of these, the Somali Wild Dog would seem to be the most distinct. In general, it may perhaps be said that animals from the southern part of the range tend to be somewhat larger in size and somewhat lighter in colour. Thus, there is more black in the coat of the Somali Wild Dog than there is in the coat of the hunting-dog from Cape Colony, while the South African animal is, on the average, an inch or so taller and some five pounds heavier.

In appearance the African Hunting-dog is a large and powerful animal, standing some twenty-six inches at the shoulder and weighing some sixty-five pounds. (The Somaliland race stands about twenty-five inches and weighs about sixty pounds.) There are only four toes to each forefoot, but the most striking characteristic is the great, upstanding, round ears. The muzzle is relatively short and broad and the limbs long and powerful, the forelegs being really massive. But the body falls away behind, and this, together with the animal's habit of carrying the head and the tail depressed when moving at ease, gives it a rather hyena-like appearance, and is responsible for the common African name, 'Hyena Dog'. It is not, of course, in any way related to the hyena, nor do its habits in any way resemble those of the true hyenas. In colouring, the hunting-dog is a tricolour, the body marked in patches of black, white and khaki. There is enormous variation in the colouring, no two animals in a pack being exactly alike. The tail is bushy, and there is a moderate throat ruff. The hunting-dog is a pack animal, living the whole of its life in company with its fellows. It is diurnal in habit, hunting for the most part at dawn and again at sunset, but also occasionally on nights of full moon. Gifted with immense speed over short distances, with remarkable scenting powers, and also with apparently limitless stamina, the hunting-dog is a very formidable factor in the wild life of Africa.

The Indian Wild Dog, or Dhole (*Cyon deccanensis*), is smaller, standing about seventeen inches at the shoulder and weighing about thirty pounds. The colour is very variable—rufous is the most common colour, but iron-grey and brindle also occur frequently; but the throat, chest and belly are almost always fawn, and the tail is usually dark with a white tip. The range of the Dhole is from Assam to Kashmir, and from Tibet to the southern tip of the continent. Naturalists have detected related races in Siberia (*Cyon alpinus*) and in Malaya (*Cyon javanicus*); but it is, perhaps, doubtful whether these deserve sub-specific status. The Dhole is also a pack animal, living the whole of its life in company with its fellows. The packs, however, are smaller than is the case with the African Hunting-dog, usually numbering about twelve and rarely exceeding a score. The packs hunt at dawn and again at sunset, but also occasionally on nights of full moon. Like the African Hunting-dog, the Dhole has remarkable scenting powers, is gifted with immense speed over a short distance, and has apparently limitless stamina. Dhole packs have been known to attack tigers and bears and to pull down buffalo. They are capable of inflicting great damage on domestic stocks; so much so, indeed, that the Government of India once offered substantial rewards for their extermination. This seems to have had little or no effect on their numbers.

The South American Bush-dog (*Icticyon venaticus*)[1] is a long-bodied, relatively short-legged animal with a short and very harsh coat. Standing only twelve inches at the shoulder, it weighs twenty-five to twenty-eight pounds; very considerably more than any fit domestic dog of the same height. The muzzle is short and broad, the ears small and pricked and the tail short and thick. There is a moderate, but still very wiry, neck ruff. The colour is very variable : brindle and black-and-tan seem to be the most common colours, but a uniform reddish-brown and a pale fawn also occur frequently. This variation has led some naturalists to recognise four 'races', but there seems to be no justification for awarding any of these sub-specific status. The range covers the wooded regions of Brazil and the Guianas and extends to Panama. Like the African Hunting-dog and the Dhole, the bush-dog is a pack animal, living the whole of its life in company with its fellows. As with the two species already considered, it hunts at dawn and again at dusk, and occasionally on nights of full moon. Remarkably little is known of its habits, however, since it is wholly a forest dweller, and therefore is rarely seen, the forests of Brazil and the Guianas being singularly inhospitable to white folk. The bush-dog is a powerful animal. Although it does not seem to possess the exceptional speed of the African Hunting-dog or the Dhole over a short distance, the natives of those areas in which it occurs are agreed that it is gifted with almost inexhaustible stamina and a wonderfully acute sense of smell. Popular estimation puts the numbers in the packs at anything from a score to over fifty.

Of the descendants of *Cynodesmus*, one branch, which was destined to become extinct, seems to have been completely North American in its distribution. This branch, the most characteristic members of which were *Hyænognathus* and *Borophagus*, followed a line of evolution which produced very large animals with heavy skulls and exceptionally strong blunt teeth. These teeth were adapted to crushing bones rather than to slashing or tearing, for these dogs were, like the modern hyenas, carrion-feeders. They were, in fact, the 'hyenas' of their time and place.[2]

[1] I am aware that some modern authorities prefer *Speothos venaticus*. In using the old, and better-known, nomenclature I have followed Dr. George Gaylord Simpson's *The Principles of Classification and a Classification of Mammals* (1945).

[2] This does not, of course, mean that they are to be related to the hyenas. It means no more than that they developed by *convergence*—because they lived very much the same sort of life as the hyenas live to-day—some similarity to hyenas. It cannot be too strongly stressed, in view of statements to the contrary

The other *Cynodesmus* branch is headed by *Tomarctus*, who may rightfully be described as the father of the modern dog family. Between *Tomarctus* and the appearance of man on earth, there were, of course, many types of dogs whose fossil remains have been found and most of which have been given imposing generic names. It is not necessary to list them all here. *Tomarctus* is the important one. *Tomarctus* must have been very like the modern dog in general appearance, for from it have sprung, with but little change in skeletal structure, the wolves and the wild dogs, the foxes and the fennecs of the modern world.

It will thus be seen that there have been four main lines of evolutionary development: the line which gave rise to the bears; the line which gave rise to the 'hyena-dogs' of North America, and which led to extinction; and the two existing lines—the one which is now represented by the hunting-dog of Africa and India and the bush-dog of South America, and the one which embraces the wolves, the wild dogs and the foxes, and which may properly be considered the trunk of the canine genealogical tree. This trunk has not grown as straight and true as, for example, the trunk of a plantation Corsican Pine, but rather (as one would, indeed, expect) in the manner of a wild woodland tree. There have been slight deviations from the perpendicular. One of these has led to the foxes or wild dogs—the Colpeo and its relatives—of South America, which are now placed by most naturalists in a sub-family, *Dusicyon*. Representatives of this sub-family were once, it would seem, widely distributed in the Old World, but are now restricted to three or four regions in the southern half of the New. The other, following a slightly different line, has led to the northern foxes and the fennecs.

But these deviations, important though they are (since they have led to successful specialised forms), are less important than the strong central trunk of the evolutionary tree. The dog tribe is a tribe of running animals, and the story of its evolution, at least from *Cynodictis* onwards, has been the story of ever-increasing perfection in this direction. To-day the dogs are more perfectly adapted in their bodily mechanism for high-speed running than any of the other carnivores with the exception of the Cheetah, which is an aberrant cat.

Many authorities maintain that it is this adaptation to running which has led to the domestication of the dog. The argument runs something

that appear from time to time even in modern books about dogs, that the hyenas are in no way related to the dogs. Although they are somewhat dog-like in appearance, the hyenas are more closely related to the cats.

like this. The adaptation to running produced in its turn a marked sociability, which in its most primitive form shows itself in a tendency to hunt, first in family parties and then in packs. Pack life in its turn produced a marked plasticity in behaviour. Co-operation between individuals in a pack demands mental adaptability, which must inevitably lead to an increase in intelligence. It was this mental adaptability which brought them into touch with man and led to their domestication.

This is, of course, a generalisation. As such, it is easy enough to pick holes in it. The foxes, for example, are strict individualists; but no one, surely, would deny that they are among the most intelligent of all the dog family. On the other hand, the foxhound is essentially a pack animal; no one, surely—except, of course, a Master of Foxhounds when discussing the merits of his own pack!—would deny that it is among the least intelligent of all dogs. Yet, as a generalisation, it is, I think, true enough. But from which member of the dog tribe does the domestic dog derive?

Obviously, in this connection we have only to consider the genus *Canis*. We can safely ignore the African Hunting-dog (*Lycaon*), the Dhole (*Cyon*), the South American Bush-dog (*Icticyon*), the South American sub-family *Dusicyon* and the foxes.[1] We are left, it would seem, with the wolves and the jackals.

The origin of the domestic dog has been the subject of argument and speculation among scientists over a very long period of time—and still is. This is not surprising when one remembers that there is archæological

[1] The fox belongs to the genus *Vulpes*. Until comparatively recently zoologists regarded it as belonging to the genus *Canis*, and it was widely supposed that some domestic dogs were descended from the fox. In fact, many people still believe that dogs and foxes will interbreed naturally when the opportunity to do so occurs. Reputed cases of dog-fox crosses are constantly being reported in the sporting Press, and I have myself in the course of the past twenty years been shown no fewer than five animals said to be the offspring of a fox and a bitch. (It is significant that I have been unable to trace, in all the voluminous literature, a single record of the cross the other way round; there is no record, so far as I am aware, of a cross between dog and vixen.) Let it be said at once that there has never been an authenticated instance of the dog and the fox having interbred. Many attempts to produce such a cross have been made in zoos and menageries, and by private persons, who have owned tame foxes; all without success. There are a number of anatomical differences between the dog and the fox. Externally, the most striking of these is that the dog's eye has a circular pupil which when contracted remains circular, while the fox has a vertically elliptical pupil which when contracted becomes a slit like that of a cat. Furthermore, it should be remembered that the gestation period of the fox is fifty to fifty-two days, whereas that in the dog is sixty-three to sixty-five days.

evidence for some association between man and dog as early as 7000 B.C. or thereabouts. As Dr. Edwin H. Colbert[1] has said:

> 'The origin of the dog is lost in the mists of antiquity, for of all the animals domesticated by man, the dog was the first. Since the time when the question of the dog's origin was first seriously investigated, numerous attempts have been made to ferret out what his ancestors might have been, but despite diligent studies towards this end no definite conclusions have been reached. Indeed, zoologists differ among themselves, and at best they can for the most part only indulge in scientific speculations regarding the ultimate ancestry of the dog.'

Despite this very fair statement of the position, Colbert himself seems to have no doubt about it:

> '. . . the domestic dog, no matter what his looks may make him, is under the skin nothing more nor less than a tractable wolf—or, to look at it from another angle, the wolf is nothing more nor less than a wild dog.'[2]

And I suppose that it would be true to say that, generally speaking, most of the authorities agree that the domestic dog is descended from the common Eurasiatic wolf (*Canis lupus*). Most, but by no means all; the jackal has its supporters. G. F. Scott Elliott,[3] an authority on prehistoric times, is among them:

> 'The dog seems to have been the very first friend of mankind, and the story of its domestication must be taken first. Both wolves and jackals occur in the middle of the Pliocene period. *Canis etruscus* was a sort of wolf, and *Canis nescherensis* may be the ancestor of the jackals. In the Ice Ages a jackal-like animal, *Canis mikii*, seems to have been in existence. Now, in India to-day, both jackals and the more or less domesticated pariah, or "pie-dog", haunt the villages, and find their unpleasant food in middens and "free cowps". We assume that the first domestication of the dog took place not in India but somewhere in Persia, or possibly Turkestan. It is extremely probable that *Canis mikii*, or something allied to it, would haunt the camps and kitchen middens of prehistoric man just as the modern jackal hangs about the outskirts of a village in India. So he may have changed

[1] *Natural History*, Vol. XLIII, No. 2, 1939. [2] *Ibid.*
[3] *Prehistoric Man and His Story* (Seeley, Service & Co.).

insensibly from the status of a wild jackal to that of a pariah dog. In Egypt, during the First Dynasty, the jackal is said to have been kept in captivity. Sooner or later prehistoric man or his children began to take interest in *Canis mikii*.

'. . . Under the conditions which would prevail in Early Neolithic or Late Paleolithic times, no sort of care would be taken in breeding the dogs of the community, and they would, in all probability, occasionally cross with the wolves or wild dogs of the district. Prince Poutiatini discovered, near Lake Bologoia in Russia, a deposit of early Post-Glacial Age which included remains of the Saiga antelope (a characteristic Steppe animal) and also of a very dog-like wolf, which has been called after him *Canis poutiatini*. . . . This may have been one of the ancestors of the Neolithic dog. . . . But it seems to us more probable that a jackal type was the first to be domesticated, and that this ancestor is responsible for the love of the ash-heap which exists in all domestic dogs.'

Gerrit S. Miller,[1] who made an exhaustive study of the anatomy of the *Canidæ*, summarily dismissed any question of relationship between the jackal and the dog after a detailed examination of the teeth, which are the most stable of all skeletal structures. He said :

'In all the dog skulls which I have examined, representing such different breeds as the pug, fox-terrier, bloodhound, mastiff, ancient Egyptian, ancient Peruvian, Eskimo (Greenland and Alaska) and American Indian, the teeth are strictly of the wolf type, never showing any approach to that of the jackal.'

F. Wood Jones,[2] who made a detailed study of the Dingo, also dismissed the jackal as a possible ancestor. He, too, based his opinion on anatomical grounds, and particularly on certain differences in the first upper molar tooth. In the jackals this tooth has a platform (the cingulum) running right round the outer side of the crown ; in the wolves the cingulum is reduced in size, and is sometimes altogether absent on the labial side of the tooth, although it is always present on the lingual side. After examining a long series of skulls of wolves and dogs, Wood Jones was convinced that the common northern (Eurasiatic) wolf (*Canis lupus*) was the only ancestor of the Dingo and the domestic dog.

[1] *Catalogue of the Mammals of Western Europe*, 1912.
[2] *The Mammals of South Australia*, 1923.

In addition to similarities in anatomical structure, there are also marked similarities in habits as between wolf and dog. These are, indeed, so obvious that they do not require the eye of a naturalist for their recognition. They struck Elisha Kent Kane,[1] who was no naturalist, so forcibly that he wrote:

> 'There is so much of identical character between our Arctic dogs and wolves that I am inclined to agree with Mr. Broderip, who in the *Zoological Revelations* assigns to them a family origin. The oblique position of the wolf's eye is not uncommon among the dogs of my team. I have a slut, one of the tamest and most affectionate of the whole of them, who has the long legs, and compact body, and drooping tail, and wild, scared expression of the eye, which some naturalists have supposed to characterize the wolf alone. When domesticated early—and it is easy to domesticate him—the wolf follows and loves you like a dog. That they are fond of a loose foot proves nothing; many of our pack will run away for weeks into the wilderness of ice; yet they cannot be persuaded when they come back to inhabit the kennel we have built for them only a hundred yards off. They crouch around for the companionship of men. Both animals howl in unison alike; the bell at the settlements of South Greenland always starts them. Their footprint is the same, at least in Smith's Sound. Nor is there anything in the supposed difference of strength. The Esquimeaux dog of Smith's Sound encounters the wolf fearlessly, with success. The wolves of Northern America never venture near the huts; but it is well known that when they have been chasing the deer or the moose, the dogs have come up as rivals in the hunt, beaten them off, and appropriated the prey themselves.'

Many other similarities in behaviour have been noted and brought forward as proof of the domestic dog's descent from the wolf. Dr. G. M. Vevers,[2] formerly Superintendent of the Zoological Society's Gardens in London, has written:

> 'The modern dog inherits many habits from the ancestral wolf; for instance, the scratching up of earth with the front feet and the pushing back of it with the hind feet, in order to cover up its tracks after micturition and defecation. Even the smallest lap-dog will turn

[1] *The Second Grimmel Expedition in Search of Sir John Franklin.*

[2] On the Phylogeny, Domestication and Bionomics of the Dog', in *The Book of the Dog*, 1948.

round and round before lying down and will sometimes scratch at the floor as if forming a nest in which to sleep. Both these habits are undoubtedly inherited from the wolf.'

Dr. Vevers, it will be seen, has not the slightest doubt about it.

There is, furthermore, not the slightest doubt that the wolf and the domestic dog will interbreed readily. These wolf-dog crosses have been known from the earliest times. Aristotle recorded wolf-dog crosses in the fourth century B.C., and Pliny, writing in the first century A.D., described how the inhabitants of Gaul would take their bitches, when in season, and tether them to trees so that they might be served by wolves. There have been innumerable similar records since, and some Eskimos are said to use a wolf-cross for their sled-dogs to this day. Between 1923 and 1930 a Russian scientist, Dr. N. A. Iljin, undertook a long series of hybridising experiments between the wolf and the dog in the Moscow Zoo Park. From these experimental matings he obtained 101 hybrids and established the following facts:

1. That wolf-dog hybrids are fully fertile.
2. That certain characteristics—hair colour and pattern, eye colour, ear form, the size of the animal, and certain skull characters—are inherited on typical Mendelian lines.
3. That there is an absolute similarity in incidence of rutting and nervous disposition.
4. That duration of pregnancy is identical.
5. That the blind period in the young is the same in both wolf and dog.
6. That the order of appearance of the milk teeth is the same in both wolf and dog.
7. That the moulting phenomena is the same in both wolf and dog.

He also proved to his satisfaction that the wild dog easily learns to bark like a domestic dog, just as the domestic dog, if placed in isolation for some time, will forget how to bark and will revert to a wolf-like howl.

Iljin[1] summed up his experiments thus:

'All these data, taken together, serve to emphasize the very close similarity in genetical constitution between the wolf and the dog, and suggest the possibility of the origin of the various races of *Canis familiaris* from a single wild species, viz. *Canis lupus*.'

[1] *The Journal of Genetics*, Vol. 43, 1941.

In view of all this, it might well be thought that the evidence in favour of the common northern (Eurasiatic) wolf (*Canis lupus*) as the sole ancestor of the domestic dog is overwhelming and that there is no room for further argument. It has, however, failed to satisfy many zoologists.

Many—indeed, it could be said all—of the similarities in behaviour between the dog and the wolf apply equally well to the jackal. Dr. Vevers has noted the habit, even in lap-dogs, of turning round and round, and sometimes scratching at the ground, before lying down, and is convinced that this behaviour has been inherited from the wolf. Charles Darwin [1] noted the habit many years ago:

> 'Dogs, when they wish to go to sleep on a carpet or other hard surface, generally turn round and round and scratch the ground with their fore-paws in a senseless manner, as if they intended to trample down the grass and scoop out a hollow, as no doubt their wild parents did, when they lived on open grassy plains or in the woods. Jackals, fennecs, and other allied animals in the Zoological Gardens treat their straw in this manner.'

It did not, it will be seen, convince him of inheritance from the wolf.

Nor is the other habit to which Dr. Vevers draws attention—that of scratching up the earth with the fore feet and pushing it back with the hind feet after micturition and defecation [2]—common to dog and wolf

[1] *The Expression of the Emotions in Man and Animals.*

[2] The usual explanation for this behaviour—that it is done to cover up tracks—does not bear investigation. Cats are very careful to bury their traces. But the most casual observation is sufficient to show that members of the dog tribe, whether domestic or wild, exercise no care at all. Indeed, the action often seems to be performed in the most aimless manner. H. M. Budgett, in his *Hunting by Scent*, 1933, has shown that crushed grass has a very lasting scent, and is convinced that the animal scratches after micturition and defecation in order to advertise its presence in the neighbourhood. E. T. Seton, who made a close study of inter-communication between animals of the dog tribe, drew attention (*Forest and Stream*, January 1897) to the signal-posts common to dogs and wolves. Foxes also have these signal-posts. Every dog-owner knows that there are certain signal-posts in his neighbourhood, and that these are regularly visited by his dog. If the aim of the scratching is to cover up traces, then the whole object of the signal-post (which is to convey information) is defeated. As it is, when the scratching is performed on grass there can be no doubt whatever that the spot is marked by a patch of scent very much more lasting than that of urine or excreta. The animal, in fact, is doing its utmost to ensure that its presence in the neighbourhood shall not be overlooked.

alone. It is common also to jackals, foxes and fennecs, and has been noted in bears.[1]

Similarly, almost all the data derived by Dr. Iljin from his hybridising experiments with wolf and dog apply equally well to jackal and dog. I must admit that I do not know—so far as I am aware, no work has been done on this—that, in the case of jackal and dog hybrids, certain characteristics are inherited on typical Mendelian lines, as is the case with wolf and dog hybrids. But it would astonish me to find that they are not. For the rest, the similarity is exact. Jackal-dog hybrids are fully fertile; the duration of pregnancy in jackal and dog is identical; the blind period in the young is the same in both jackal and dog; the moulting phenomena is the same in both; and there is an absolute similarity in incidence of rutting and nervous disposition. Furthermore, the jackal, unlike the wolf but like the dog, can both bark and howl.

One point which is always advanced in favour of the wolf as the ancestor of the domestic dog is that the wolf is a 'pack animal'. These wolf packs are said to operate under the direction of a leader and to be capable of elaborate co-operation. In this connection, Dr. Edwin Colbert[2] has written:

> 'The tales of hunting by relays are so often told as to be almost trite. A number of wolves or wild dogs will map out a "course" over which the quarry is to be pursued. Then several dogs will distribute themselves along this course—usually circular—and take their turns in chasing the antelope or deer, until the animal is fatigued to a point of exhaustion.'

Indeed, the cunning of the wolf is, on occasion, carried to much greater lengths than this, for we are assured that, when they wish to conceal their exact numbers, the pack 'travels in single file, one animal treading in the footsteps made by another in the snow'.[3] Moreover, the spirit of co-operation within the pack is so highly developed that 'there are well-authenticated records of wolves supplying food for an infirm and aged member of the pack'.[4] All this—and most of the rest of wolf lore—is legend.[5] A man who spent the whole of his life in the Arctic, and

[1] V. K. Arseniev, *Dersu the Trapper*, 1939.

[2] *Natural History*, Vol. XLIII, 1939.

[3] F. Alverdes, *Social Life in the Animal World.*

[4] E. H. Colbert, *Natural History*, Vol. XLIII, 1939. N.B.—I have spent many years, without success, trying to find one authentic record.

[5] For a complete *exposé* of the legend, see Bergen Evans, *The Natural History of Nonsense*, 1947.

who probably had a closer acquaintance with and deeper knowledge of wolves in their natural state than any other white man before or since, Vilhjalmur Stefansson,[1] has placed it on record that he has never seen a pack of wolves, that he has never seen a greater number of wolves in association than the mother and cubs of one family. Dr. E. W. Nelson,[2] a former Chief of the United States Biological Survey, agreed with Stefansson that wolf packs are legendary.

From all this and despite the evidence of the teeth, it would seem that the scales are fairly evenly balanced, that one may take one's choice of wolf and jackal as the ancestor of the domestic dog.

One modern scientist, Dr. Konrad Z. Lorenz, seeking the best of both worlds, maintains that some domestic dogs are descended from the wolf and others from the jackal, with strikingly different results in canine personality. He believes that the wolf was the common northern (Eurasiatic) wolf (*Canis lupus*); the jackal, the Oriental or Golden Jackal (*Canis aureus*). He says [3] :

> 'The northern wolf (*Canis lupus*) only figures in the ancestry of our present dog breeds through having been crossed with already domesticated Aureus dogs. Contrary to the wide-spread opinion that the wolf plays an essential role in the ancestry of the larger dog breeds, comparative research in behaviour has revealed the fact that all European dogs, including the largest ones, such as Great Danes and wolfhounds, are pure Aureus and contain, at the most, a minute amount of wolf's blood. The purest wolf-dogs that exist are certain breeds of Arctic America, particularly the so-called malemuts, huskies, etc. The Esquimaux dogs of Greenland also show but slight traces of Lapland Aureus characters, whereas the arctic breeds of the Old World, such as Lapland dogs, Russian lajkas, samoyedes and chow-chows, certainly have more Aureus in their constitution.'

It should be pointed out here that this view is very far, very far indeed, from generally accepted. Even should it be broadly correct, then the common northern wolf cannot be responsible for the breeds of Arctic America, for *Canis lupus* does not occur anywhere in the New World; nor is there any record of its ever having done so.

Dr. Lorenz bases his belief in the strikingly different canine personali-

[1] *The Friendly Arctic*, 1924, and *Adventures in Error*, 1936.
[2] *Adventures in Error*, 1936.
[3] *King Solomon's Ring*, 1952.

ties of the two streams—there are those who would not agree that there is, in fact, any striking difference—on the following:

> 'One essential difference in the character of Lupus and Aureus dogs is attributable to the fact that these two springs flow with different strength in the two types. In the life of a wolf, the community of the pack plays a vastly more important role than in that of a jackal. While the latter is essentially a solitary hunter and confines himself to a limited territory, the wolf packs roam far and wide through the forests of the North as a sworn and very exclusive band which sticks together through thick and thin and whose members will defend each other to the very death.' [1]

Well, we have already seen how much reliance can be placed on the story of the wolf pack. And Dr. Lorenz, who here speaks of the jackal as a 'solitary hunter', but a page or two earlier in the same chapter speaks of 'the pack of jackals'.

In his more recent book [2] Dr. Lorenz has shifted his ground slightly. He is still convinced that the northern wolf is not the ancestor of most of our domestic dogs, but he is less certain about the Oriental or Golden Jackal. I quote:

> 'At the same time, we must not conceal the fact that we do not know for certain that it was exclusively the golden jackal (*Canis aureus*) that attached itself to man in the way described. It is indeed very probable that in different parts of the earth various larger and wolf-like species of jackal became domesticated and later interbred, just as many other forms of domesticated animals originate from more than one wild progenitor. A very strong argument in favour of this theory is that pariah dogs do not at all tend to mingle and to re-cross with the wild Canis aureus. Mr. Shebbeare has very kindly drawn my attention to the fact that there are lots of localities in the near East where Pie-dogs and golden jackals abound, yet never intermingle. However, it is quite certain that the northern wolf is not the ancestor of most of our domestic dogs as was formerly believed.'

This seems to be no more than a restatement of the old theory of polyphyletic origin. It is, of course, none the worse for that.

Two great difficulties have always faced those who seek to discover the origin of the domestic dog: the domestic dogs of the American

[1] *King Solomon's Ring*, 1952. [2] *Man Meets Dog*, 1954.

continent, and the many and great variations in size and appearance of the different breeds of dogs.

The domestic dogs of America provide a very formidable obstacle. Man, we now know, has been on the American continent for some ten thousand years. Folsom Man is dated to approximately ten thousand years ago, and we know that there were men in Oregon, in Mexico and in Peru at about the same time. Archæological research has shown that there were men living as far south as the Magellan Straits nine thousand years ago. But no trace of man has been discovered on the east coast of the continent earlier than five thousand years ago. Oregon man was advanced enough to make woven fibre sandals with handsome patterns, but he does not appear to have known the domestic dog. Nor is there any evidence that Folsom Man, or early man in Mexico, Peru and the Straits of Magellan, had domesticated the dog. If the Oriental Jackal or the Northern Wolf is the ancestor of the domestic dog, then it must have been brought into America later, since neither of these wild species occur anywhere on the American continent. Archæology has not, however, yet produced evidence for this. The one undeniable fact is that, when Euopeans first reached the American continent they found the dog domesticated. And it is evident from their writings that in the big centres of civilisation—Mexico and Peru—it had been domesticated for a very long time. Furthermore, the Red Indian 'savage' had the domestic dog, as John Richardson[1] tells us :

> 'This variety of dog is cultivated at present, so far as I know, only by the Hare Indians, and other tribes that frequent the borders of the Great Bear Lake and the banks of the Mackenzie. It is used by them solely in the chase, being too small to be useful as a beast of burden or draught. The Hare Indian dog has a mild countenance, with, at times, an expression of demureness. It has a small head, slender muzzle; erect, thickish ears; somewhat oblique eyes; rather slender legs, and a broad hairy foot with a bushy tail, which it usually carries curled over its right hip. It is covered with long hair. The size of the Hare Indian dog is inferior to that of the prairie wolf, but rather exceeds that of the red American fox.'

That animal, if it was descended from either the Oriental Jackal or the Northern Wolf, would seem to have come a very long way indeed.

The theory of polyphyletic origin was advanced—originally by

[1] *The Zoology of the Northern Parts of British America.*

Charles Darwin[1]—to account for the world-wide distribution of, and enormous variation in, the domestic dog. It postulates that the domestic dogs of Asia are descended from the wild dogs of Asia, the domestic dogs of North America from the wild dogs of North America, those of South America from the wild dogs of South America and so on. Gerrit S. Miller[2] would have none of this:

> 'Prevalent though this belief may be, it probably rests on no secure basis of facts. Superficial resemblances in general form, in colour, and in quality of fur, to jackals, coyotes, foxes and other wild members of the family may not infrequently be seen in domestic dogs. But in all the specimens I have examined, representing very diversified breeds, the skull and teeth remain fundamentally true to the type which in wild canids is peculiar to the northern wolves. This type, particularly as regards the cheek teeth, does not represent a primitive condition which might be expected to occur in various members of the family without having any special significance. On the contrary, in respect to the development of a combined cutting and crushing type of carnassials and molars it is the most highly specialised now in existence. It is, as I have said, not known outside of the restricted genus or subgenus *Canis*. Dogs, which were certainly not carried by modern Europeans, accompany native man in many parts of the world, Africa, Malaya, Australia and South America for instance, where no true *Canis* is known to occur now or to have occurred in the past, and all of them apparently retain these generic or subgeneric characters uncontaminated by those of their local relatives with which they have been brought in contact. The best explanation of all these conditions seems to be that dogs were originally domesticated somewhere within the northern area inhabited by the true *Canis*, and that they were subsequently taken by man into most of the regions into which he has penetrated. Wherever dogs and wild *Canis* in the restricted sense occur together, crossing may take place, and by this process many, possibly all, local forms of the wolf have perhaps contributed to the peculiarity of the domestic races. At present, however, there seems to be no satisfactory evidence of polyphyletic origin of any other kind.'

[1] *Variation of Animals and Plants under Domestication.*
[2] *Journal of Mammalogy*, Vol. 1.

Arnolfini and his Wife by Jan van Eyck.

Philip and Mary by Antonio Moro.

A more recent authority, C. R. Stockard,[1] has revived the theory of the polyphyletic origin of the domestic dog, basing his argument on genetical grounds. He conducted a long series of matings between achrondoplasic [2] breeds—such as the Bulldog, the Pekingese, the Dachshund and so on—and breeds having no skeletal defects. These experimental crossings convinced him that there must have been a number of different species involved to produce so many variations. But—though he proved beyond all question that the achondroplasic factor, where it affects the legs or the muzzle, is dominant—he failed to convert scientists to the polyphyletic theory, for the very sound reason that he ignored altogether the anatomical work of Miller and Wood Jones, and especially their meticulously detailed work relating to the teeth. Dr. G. M. Vevers [3] is emphatic in his rejection of the theory:

> '*This theory of polyphyletic origin has no scientific basis of truth.* . . . It does not follow that because a breed of dog may superficially resemble a fox or jackal or some other wild species of the *Canidæ*, it is necessarily descended from that species. It was on superficial resemblances, such as coat colour, carriage of ears and tail and other obvious but plastic features, that the earlier writers based their theory of the polyphyletic origin of the dog. An enquiry into the detailed anatomy of the structure of the skull and teeth has proved conclusively that they were wrong.'

The italics, incidentally, are his.

Now, what is one to make of all this contradictory material? I think that, despite Dr. Lorenz's persuasive arguments, one must discard the findings of 'comparative research in behaviour'. One cannot discard the anatomical evidence. If one does do so, then one must at the same time discard the whole theory of evolution, for one cannot accept anatomical evidence for one species and reject it for another. On the anatomical evidence we must reject the jackal (*Canis aureus*). It would seem, therefore, that we are left with the common northern wolf (*Canis lupus*) as the sole ancestor of the domestic dog—and, at the same time, with a lot of apparently insoluble problems. These problems are such as to make it impossible for many thinking people—even while they are prepared to

[1] *The Genetic and Endocrinic Basis for Differences in Form and Behaviour* (Wistar Institute of Anatomy and Biology, Philadelphia, 1941).

[2] Achondroplasia is a congenital disease of the growing bones in which the cartilage does not develop, resulting in shortening and deformity of the bones.

[3] *On the Phylogeny, Domestication and Bionomics of the Dog.*

reject the jackal—to accept the anatomical evidence for *Canis lupus* at its face value.

Consider, first, the question of domestication itself. How did the dog first become domesticated? Any number of writers have put forward theories as to how this was first accomplished, and many of these imaginative accounts are most beautifully written, notably Dr. Lorenz's[1] for the first steps in the domestication of the jackal. Although I am compelled, on the anatomical evidence, to reject the jackal, I find this account much more convincing than any I have yet read for the first domestication of the wolf. For all of these presuppose characters and habits in the wolf which do not exist, at least in the modern *Canis lupus*. Dr. G. M. Vevers[2] says:

> 'It may be that the scavenging habits of the wolf in the neighbourhood of human habitations led to young individuals being caught and treated as pets, with the result that within a few generations this very adaptable creature came to rely on man for food and shelter. Anyone who has had experience in rearing young wolves will know how easily they are tamed and taught to be obedient.'

M. F. Ashley Montague[3] does not agree that domestication came about through cubs being caught and treated as pets. He believes (and history supports him) that the pet is a relatively recent development of civilisation. He suggests that domestication came about through the scavenging habits of the animal being enlisted in the service of man:

> 'The earliest human groups were food-gatherers and hunters, with no agriculture or domestic animals of any sort. Living a semi-nomadic existence in search of food they would occupy a site until the food supply was dangerously diminished, whereupon they would move to another area where the food was more abundant. At each of their camps or settlements they would throw the remains of their meals into heaps which often assumed considerable dimensions, depending upon the length of their stay and the numbers in the group. The odour from these middens must often have been quite overpowering. Hence, when it was discovered that the dog was a willing consumer of the left-overs from "kitchen" and "table" who would thus effectively serve to

[1] *Man Meets Dog.*
[2] *On the Phylogeny, Domestication and Bionomics of the Dog.*
[3] 'On the Origin of the Domestication of the Dog,' *Science*, Vol. 42, 1942.

eliminate the intolerable odours which blew in from the refuse heaps, his assistance was permanently enlisted in this worthy task.'

Wood Jones[1] is of the same opinion:

'Dogs were domesticated comparatively early in man's history, and they probably have this peculiarity in their domestication—that they did not become friends of man on a sudden, by reason of captivity, but rather they passed through successive stages of camp-follower, hanger-on, dependant, and finally companion.'

It seems to me that Wood Jones and Ashley Montague have the truth of the matter. But is *Canis lupus* a scavenger in the neighbourhood of human habitations? Was it ever so? The habit, surely, is that of the jackal; and we know that the jackal cannot have been the ancestor of the domestic dog.

There is, moreover, another point, one that is too frequently forgotten —that of domestication itself. There is all the difference in the world between 'taming' an animal and 'domesticating' an animal. The two are too often confused.

It is perfectly true, as Dr. Vevers has pointed out, that wolf cubs are easily tamed and taught to be obedient. As a matter of fact, there are remarkably few wild animals the young of which are quite untamable. But generations of taming these tamable young in captivity will not produce a domestic species. Indeed, the experiment has been tried. Geoffroy St. Hilaire founded the Jardin d'Acclimatation in Paris for this precise purpose. He proposed to produce a number of new domestic breeds, useful to man, by breeding tamed members of suitable wild species and their offspring through several generations. No new domestic breeds were produced.

Tameness in itself does not lead to domesticity. Man has been using the elephant for hundreds of years. The elephant is a highly intelligent and exceptionally adaptable creature, easily taught and capable of great affection towards its keeper. But, despite its long association with man, the elephant remains a wild animal. Each young elephant has to be tamed afresh. Lions have been kept in captivity for centuries. They breed readily in captivity, and the cubs are not difficult to tame. For that matter, many hundreds of grown animals have been tamed in circuses and elsewhere, and more than one lion has been trained to the lead and

[1] *The Mammals of South Australia.*

regarded as a household pet. But the tamest lioness will teach her cubs to beware of man, even of the man who feeds and cares for her and with whom she is the greatest friend. The lion remains a wild animal. So, too, with the fox. It is easy enough to tame a fox cub. But a tame vixen will teach her cubs to beware of her human friends. The cubs will be wild, and each will have to be tamed individually. And it is the same with the wolf. It is easy enough to tame a wolf cub. But nobody has ever bred a tame wolf. The wolf remains a wild animal. Centuries of breeding in captivity has made not the slightest difference. Something more than tameness is required. As Dr. A. L. Hagedoorn[1] has put it: 'Domestic animals differ from wild species in their genotype, in their inherited constitution.'

Moreover, this difference in genotype, this inherited constitution for domesticity, inevitably leads, it would seem—at least in mammals—to extinction as a genuinely wild species. There are now no wild horses, the ancestor of the domestic cow has disappeared, there are now no wild camels anywhere in the world and so on. Had *Canis lupus* been domesticated all those thousands of years ago, it would, surely, long since have disappeared as a wild species.[2]

Since we know that the jackal (*Canis aureus*) could not, on anatomical grounds, have been the ancestor of the domestic dog, and since *Canis lupus* does not fit the pattern in a number of respects, might it not be possible that the domestic dog has descended from some other animal, neither wolf nor jackal, but a wild dog? Might it not be possible that we have all the time, before our very eyes, the spring from which has flowed the domestic dog in all its many forms? I believe it to be possible, and I refer to the Pariah Dog.

Although there is no better known dog in the Orient, although no animal is more frequently described in books of travel, the Pariah or Pi Dog—the spelling 'Pie' is, I am assured by Orientalists, incorrect—is dismissed as a 'mongrel stray', an ownerless street-dog, a canine outcast, by the vast majority of dog lovers and has been ignored for the most part by the scientists for the same reason. The idea that the Pariah Dog is a

[1] *Animal Breeding*, 1939.

[2] I am well aware that the Caffre Cat (*Felis ocreata*), which is regarded by many naturalists as one of the sources—it is certainly not the sole source—of the modern house cat, is common in the wild state. But the house cat is not truly a domesticated animal. The true domestic animal is dependent upon man; the cat is not. The cat accepts man as a companion, but remains essentially a wild animal, very well able to support itself.

mongrel stray was given authority by Robert Leighton,[1] although it was not he that first gave the notion currency:

> 'Pariah dogs are to be found in almost all Oriental towns prowling about their own particular encampment, and in a measure protecting the greater encampments of their human friends. Primarily they are not wild dogs attracted towards the dwellings of men by an easy means of obtaining food, but descendants of the sentinel and scavenger dogs of a nomad race, domestic dogs which have degenerated into semi-wildness, yet which remain, as by inherited habit, in association with mankind. They vary considerably according to their abode, and there is no fixed type: they are all mongrels. But by the process of indiscriminate interbreeding and the influence of environment, they acquire local character which may often be mistaken for type.'

Leighton was the recognised authority at the turn of the century, and his views were generally accepted without question. About the Pariah, at least, he was wrong. By no means all the ownerless street-dogs of the Orient are Pariahs, and by no means all Pariah dogs are town dogs. On the contrary, but a small percentage of them live in towns. Moreover, of those that do, by no means all are ownerless; many are owned and kept as house-dogs. And the true Pariah is certainly not a mongrel.

As the Drs. Menzel[2] have pointed out, the Pariah, so far from being a mongrel stray, is a well-defined form of *Canis familiaris*, a group of natural breeds which has remained relatively pure-bred. The degree to which any group, in any region, remains more or less unmixed depends upon the presence in that region of European breeds, since there is always the possibility of crossing with the latter, though this does not occur nearly so frequently as might be imagined.

The range of the Pariah dog extends from Morocco to the Far East. It occurs throughout North Africa, the Near East and southern Asia, in Indonesia and Australia, in China and Japan. In Europe it was present in southern Spain until comparatively recently, and it is still relatively common in Greece, Albania, Bulgaria, Turkey and the Caucasus. Moreover, dogs of a Pariah type and habit are still to be found in many parts of South and Central America.

[1] *The New Book of the Dog*, 1907.

[2] 'Observations on the Pariah Dog,' by R. and R. Menzel, *The Book of the Dog*, 1948.

Leighton[1] describes the Pariah as 'about the size of the Collie, resembling the Dingo, tawny in colour, with a furry coat, a bushy tail, and pointed ears'. This is a woefully inadequate description. The Menzels,[2] who have done more detailed work over a longer period on the Pariah than anyone else, recognise five distinct types :

I. Heavy extreme type (Sheepdog-like).
II. Heavy medium type (Dingo-like).
III. Light medium type (Collie-like).
IV. Light extreme type (Greyhound-like).
V. Small-grown type.

At the same time they point out that it would be quite impossible to make an arbitrary division into groups 'as there are so many variations and intermediates between the different types that specimens could, in fact, be displayed in a continuous sequence, leading from the sheepdog-like (Type I) through the two medium types to the greyhound-like (Type IV)'.

Nevertheless, these distinct types exist, and are common and easily recognisable. The Menzels,[3] whose work was done in Israel, describe Type I as having :

> 'a compact and more or less square-shaped body, with short back, short neck and a clumsy head, which, seen from above, appears pear-shaped. The skull is broad, with a moderate stop and a relatively short and broad muzzle. . . . The tail is bushy, and is carried, under excitement, curled across the back. Colour is generally white or yellow, but black or spotted animals are occasionally found. The hair varies in type from waved to woolly, and is smooth and short; the ears are hardly ever pricked, but vary in shape from button-ears to hanging-ears.'

And they go on to say that they have found among Pariahs of this type dogs which, so far as habitat and appearance are concerned, might be links with the Old English Sheepdog, the Russian Owtscharka, the

[1] *The New Book of the Dog*, 1907.
[2] 'Observations on the Pariah Dog,' by R. and R. Menzel, *The Book of the Dog*, 1948.
[3] *Ibid.*

Hungarian Komondor, the Italian Sheepdogs, the Caucasian Mountain-dog and the Kurdic Sheepdog.

Type II is described as a lighter form of Type I. Here again the skull, viewed from above, is pear-shaped, the skull being considerably broader than the muzzle. The dogs in this group are rather short-legged, and the hair is rough, long, straight and stiff. Some of the dogs in this group are prick-eared or semi-prick-eared, and 'fluctuate in appearance between the Dingo and the Arctic sledge-dogs (Eskimo-dogs, Samoyeds, etc.)—in fact, in pictures it is sometimes difficult to distinguish them from the latter'.

The dogs of Type III are described as being 'the aristocratic form of Type II'. They are most easily compared with a medium-coated collie, and vary in type between the collie and the Arctic sledge-dog. Again they are square in build, but with the belly 'tucked up' under the loins. Many have a typical mane, and, even when short-haired, a more or less bushy tail which, when the animal is excited, is carried curled over the back. The head is more elongated than in Type II, and the muzzle is lighter.

Colour in both these medium types is very variable. White, sandy, fawn, red-brown, black, black-and-tan and grey all occur. And all these colours can be found mixed with white markings. Yellow dogs sometimes have black muzzles, and brindles are also occasionally seen.

Type IV is almost always short-haired, though sometimes feathered. The head is typically greyhound, elongated, with a narrow skull and a relatively long muzzle. The ears vary from a hanging-ear to a rose ear; prick-ears are very uncommon, but do occur occasionally. The colour is variable, and probably all the colours mentioned for Types II and III occur, but sandy and yellow are the common colours. The body shape is often so typically greyhound that, in photographs, no difference is apparent.

Type V the Menzels describe as comprised of 'animals similar in all respects to the medium types and varying between the heavy and light forms, while being in the main considerably smaller in size than the normal Pariah dog. We reject most definitely the theory that it is a "starvation-form" of the Pariah, as we have seen many well-developed and well-nourished specimens, and are confident that its smallness of form is due to some hereditary quality of size.'

Pariahs of this 'small-grown' type often bear a striking likeness to the Basenji, the bush-dog of the Congo basin, which has recently enjoyed some popularity in Britain and the United States. It is worth while remembering that many dogs of this type are to be found in Africa leading a feral or semi-feral existence. Indeed, although the Menzels worked in Israel, it would be a grave mistake to imagine that their five types are confined to the Near East. They are to be found throughout the range of the Pariah dog. And it seems probable that, at one time, all of them may have occurred in the New World as well. It should not be forgotten that the first Spaniards in the islands of the Caribbean found there greyhound-like dogs—these were, surely, the ancestors of the San Domingo greyhounds mentioned by Buffon—and in Mexico a small feral dog, known as the Yzicuinte, which from Recchi's picture might very well pass for a small Basenji.

No matter what the type or the habitat, throughout its range the habits of the Pariah dog are very much the same. Leighton[1] says:

> 'Everywhere they gather in separate communities restricted by recognised frontiers beyond which they never stray, and into which the dogs of no other community are permitted to enter. Everywhere each separate pack has its chosen leader or sentinel who is followed and obeyed and who alone has the privilege of challenging the leader of a rival pack and of keeping his subjects within bounds.'

This statement is not altogether accurate. The 'chosen leader' is on a par with the 'grizzled leader' of the wolf pack. It would be more accurate to say that there is a pack discipline which is obeyed by its members. And it is certainly not true to say that Pariahs always live in packs. In a large city (and Leighton's acquaintance with the Pariah seems to have been confined to Istanboul) it is, of course, the pack rather than the individual dog that is noticeable. But, though the pack is a common feature in the life of the Pariah, throughout its range many Pariahs are to be found leading solitary lives. It would, however, be true to say that territory imposes a community bond. Solitary animals may live within the territory of a pack and, should they do so, will be unmolested. In their turn, they will join with the pack to repel any intruder from another territory. The territory imposes a sort of social conscience. Solitary or not, the Pariah is a social animal.

The defence of territory is very thorough. Turning to Leighton[2] again, we find:

[1] *The New Book of the Dog.* [2] *Ibid.*

> 'This separation into packs is one of the most curious characteristics of these dogs. They keep strictly within the bounds of their own quarter, and if one dares to stray into a rival camp he is immediately attacked, and probably killed.'

But there is sometimes, curiously enough, a partial breakdown in the rigidity of this behaviour. The Menzels[1] have noticed that during the rutting season males sometimes come in from other territories. Savage fights occur when this happens, but during the rut these intruders are not attacked by the pack as a whole (as would be the case out of the rut) but only by individual members. If the intruder is able to establish himself, he is permitted to join the procession of sexually-excited dogs following the bitch on heat. As soon as the rut is over these intruders make haste to return to their own territories, for should they not do so disaster would overtake them. During the rut the bitch will, of course, be covered by one male after another in the order of precedence decided by the preliminary fighting, and this, naturally, helps to account for the diversity of types. Precisely the same behaviour is to be noticed in the 'uncontrolled' matings of the domestic dog.

It is apparent from the majority of the dog books—and this despite Leighton (who has been slavishly copied in most other respects)—that there exist many grave misconceptions about the temperament of the Pariah dog. But let Leighton[2] speak for himself:

> 'It is the common custom to speak and write of Pariah dogs as diseased and detestable scavengers, feeding on garbage, snarling and snapping at all strangers, and making night hideous by their unearthly howling. But no lover of dogs can live for any time in an eastern city such as Constantinople without being intensely interested in these despised and rejected waifs. Studying them for their points, he will acknowledge that when in good condition many of them are handsome beasts, not wholly destitute of the qualities desired in the more favoured breeds. Studying them for their habits, he will discover what is often missed by the inattentive observer, that they have characteristics meriting admiration rather than disgust and contempt.
>
> 'They are not scavengers in the literal sense. They do not feed on filth and offal, but merely select such scraps as serve their purpose out of the dustbins placed at night outside the door of every house to

[1] *Observations on the Pariah Dog.* [2] *The New Book of the Dog.*

be removed in the early morning. . . . Where Pariahs are not ill-used they are rarely aggressive and often very sociable, and when kindly notice is taken of them they will return the civility with a canine caress. . . . The Pariah dog never attempts to enter a dwelling, but will patiently wait outside until the expected food is brought out. . . . Instances have been known of Pariah dogs chivalrously protecting the pet dog of persons who have been kind to them. It is rarely that anyone is bitten by them, although they may snap when kicked or trodden upon.'

Though coloured with the false sentiment which is unfortunately all too prevalent among dog-lovers—the habits of humans and animals should never be confused, for their worlds are entirely different; what is 'filth' to a human is not necessarily filth to a dog; the natural habits of an animal never merit 'disgust and contempt'—this is an accurate picture of the character and temperament of the Pariah dog. A much earlier authority noticed two other qualities. Hamilton Smith,[1] writing in 1838, spoke of the Pariah dog as being 'sagacious and cowardly'. Of its sagacity no one can have the least doubt. 'Cowardly', however, is the wrong word; 'cautious' would be a better one.

Considering all these factors—habits, character, temperament—is it not evident that we have here the essence of the domestic dog? Do not all these factors fit the domestic dog very much more closely than do the habits, character and temperament of the wolf or the jackal? I do not think that there can be any doubt about it. And, of course, the similarity has often been noticed before. Strebel,[2] for example, was so struck by the similarity between the Menzels' Type I and the sheepdog that he was convinced that it must have been derived from the German shepherd-dog. It does not seem to have occurred to him (nor, indeed, to the vast majority of the scientists) that it might have been the other way round: that the German shepherd-dog might have been derived from the Pariah Type I. Yet, considering the vast range of the Pariah Type I, this is, surely, more probable. The fact is that we are not conditioned to expect in a wild or semi-wild animal the characters and qualities of the domestic dog, and, when we find them there, we leap to the conclusion, without the least justification, that the domestic dogs must originally have been responsible for them. And when we find that the Pariah dog, when

[1] *Jardine's Naturalist's Library,* Vol. XIX, 1839.
[2] *Die deutschen Hunde und ihre Abstammung* (Munich, N.D.).

tamed, is a magnificent watch-dog (it is used as such by native peoples here and there throughout the range); that it can be trained as an excellent herd-dog (the Bedouin, among others, use it for this purpose); that it can be used for hunting game (and is so used by native people here and there throughout the range); and that it can be trained for tracking and mine-detecting work (the Menzels have tamed wild adults and trained them for this work with great success)—well, then we take it as incontrovertable evidence that the Pariah is nothing more than a domestic strain (preferably of European origin!) gone feral.

Only Studer[1] (definitely) and Hauck[2] (rather tentatively) have considered the Pariah as the source of the domestic dog. Studer wrote:

> 'From the time of the Flood there existed a type of *Canides* (*Canis ferus*) smaller than the wolf, distributed in the same area, but exceeding it in number in the South, consequently spreading as far as the Australian continent. . . .'

Hilzheimer,[3] who also made a study of the Pariah, dismissed *Canis ferus*, stating that there was no evidence for its existence, but he (and also Antonius[4]) admitted that, of all forms living to-day, the Pariah was the most akin to a hypothetic wild-dog ancestor.

I do not think that we need take the lack of palæontological evidence for the existence of a *Canis ferus* very seriously. Indeed, I am not convinced that there is, in fact, any lack of such evidence. The fossil remains of many forms of wild dogs have been found. So much depends on a mere name, and, for that matter, on the whim of the scientist responsible for the naming.

But the evidence on the other side seems to me to be very strong. Here we have an animal whose teeth satisfy the anatomists. Here we have a wild animal with all the basic habits of the domestic dog, and one, moreover, that, while exhibiting the caution typical of a wild animal, shows no fear of man and has some liking for the neighbourhood of his dwellings. And here we have a wild animal with the difference in genotype which Hagedoorn maintains is essential in any wild animal before domestication is possible. The great difference between the Pariah and the wolf or the jackal is that, while both wolf and jackal can be tamed

[1] *Die praehistischen Hunde* (Zurich, 1901).
[2] *Die Beurteilung des Hundes* (Vienna, 1929).
[3] *Naturliche Rassengeschichte der Haussaeugetiere* (Leipzig, 1926).
[4] *Grundzuege einer Stammesgeschichte der Haustiere* (Jena, 1912).

(and even, on occasions, trained), their young are born wild and continue to be born wild even after generations of breeding between tamed adults, whereas the Pariah cannot only be tamed and trained (even, on occasions, as adults), but the young, after only two or three generations, are born tame. Furthermore, the Menzels, from the depth of their great experience, believe that it would be possible to breed out of Pariah dogs, and in a comparatively short time—every known type of domestic dog.

II

FIRST DOMESTICATION AND EARLY HISTORY

THE spade and the pick have revealed the fossil remains of many *Canidæ*, which have been separated by the taxonomists into some fifty-six genera. Fossil canids, mostly in fragmentary form, are indeed abundant. But this richness of material has proved an embarrassment to the scientists, since it has served to complicate rather than to elucidate the subdivisions of the family. Without specialised training, no man can hope to follow the taxonomists (to whom argument appears to be the very breath of life) through their neat but endless bickerings, for even where—as is more often than not the case—the genus is agreed, there is as often as not disagreement about its membership.

Scott Elliott, for example, considered *Canis mikii* to be a jackal: Woldrich considered it to be a true dog. Woldrich also considered *Canis hycernicus* a true dog: Doderlein was certain that it was a fox. Jeitteles[1] was quite sure that his *Canis matris optimæ*, 'the best mother dog', was not only a true dog but the ancestor of many modern breeds: Matschie was equally convinced that it was a jackal. And so one could go on. Even the best known of all European prehistoric forms, the Marsh Dog of the Swiss lake-dwellings (*Canis familiaris palustris*), has had doubt cast upon it, although there is in this case a complete skeleton available for examination. Studer considered it to be distinctly fox-like, and a great modern

[1] *Die Stamen Vater unserer Hunderassen* (Dresden, 1877).

authority, the late Edward Ash,[1] thought it very likely that the skeleton is that of a fossil fox. It will be seen that the fossil *Canidæ* are best left alone by the amateur.

But such is the enthusiasm generated by the dog in its historians that almost all of them have accepted without question all these fossil *Canidæ* as true dogs. Several have gone further and have traced modern breeds back to them. For example, one modern historian, in a recently published book, asserts that *Canis mikii* was the ancestor of *Canis matris optimæ*, that *C. m. optimæ* was the ancestor of *Canis familiaris palustris*, and that *C. f. palustris* was the ancestor of all modern shepherd-dogs. This is not history but fiction.

The same author, in his desire—a desire common to many canine historians—to give the modern domestic dog as ancient a lineage as possible, has gone back to the Lower Pliocene and *Simocyon* for the ancestor of other modern breeds. He maintains that there were two types of *Simocyon*, a small variety (*Simocyon primigenius*) and a larger and heavier variety (*Simocyon diaphorus*), and that the Pug is descended from the former, while the Mastiff and the St. Bernard are descended from the latter. This is pure fantasy.[2]

It is apparent that many of the historians, in their anxiety to endow the domestic dog with an ancient lineage, have confused 'association' with 'domestication'. There is ample and undeniable evidence of some association between primitive man and some member, or members, of the *Canidæ*. But the inference drawn from this evidence by Robert Leighton and many others is quite unjustifiable. Leighton[3] says:

> 'Convincing evidence of the friendship between the *Canidæ* and primitive man is to be found in the remains left by the ancient cave-dwellers, where the half-petrified bones of men and dogs are mingled, and the prehistoric savages of Northern Europe have left many such silent mementoes of the past which enable us to gain an insight into the conditions of their daily life and their domestication of animals. In the Danish "Kitchen-middens", or heaps of household refuse, piled up by the men of the Newer Stone Age—an age when

[1] *Dogs: Their History and Development*, 1927.

[2] It is true that *Simocyon* was discovered as a fossil in Europe. It is true that there is a modern sub-family of the *Canidæ* known as the *Simocyoninæ*. But its three living representatives are not generically distinct from their fossil ancestor. These three are the African Hunting-dog, the Dhole and the South American Bush-dog.

[3] *The New Book of the Dog*, 1907.

> these Neolithic peoples used chipped or polished flints instead of metal for their weapons—are found bone remnants belonging to some species of the genus *Canis*.'

But this is not proof of friendship. It is not even proof of domestication. It is proof of association. But no more than that, for it may well be that the bones are in the caves and in the kitchen-middens simply because dogs were eaten by primitive man. Dogs are still eaten by man in many parts of the world.

The idea of the dog as an article of food is repugnant to modern Englishmen. And it is noticeable that most English historians of the dog are at pains to stress not only their subject's ancient lineage as a domestic animal, but also man's ancient lineage as a dog-lover. The Stone Age dog, we are assured, was 'temperamentally trustful and friendly, and liked to be petted'. The implication, of course, is that Stone Age man—English Stone Age man, at any rate—was a friendly soul who liked to pet his dog. It really is astonishing how much information can be obtained from a fossil skull.

The oldest known British dog dates from about 1750 B.C. It was discovered in 1928 during the excavations of the Windmill Hill site near Avebury. The unusually perfect skeleton, which has often been described as resembling a long-legged Fox Terrier, is in the Avebury Museum. It does not appear to me to resemble a Fox Terrier in any way at all. Relatively to the length of the back, the skull is just about the same length as that of a Dingo, and the skeleton seems to me to be very much that of a Dingo. Something of the same idea seems to have been in the mind of Professor D. M. S. Watson, F.R.S., who made a detailed examination of the skeleton shortly after excavation and who noted affinities with *Canis familiaris palustris*, the dog of the Swiss lake-dwellings, for he remarked that the 'Windmill Hill dog does not appear to be specialised for any particular function, and was a watch-dog or hunting-dog, the companion and friend of his owner, very much as is the dingo to this day to the Australian aboriginal'. Probably it had attained about the same stage of domestication as the Australian aboriginal's dog.

The peoples of the Bronze Age, and especially those of the late Bronze Age, cultivated land and kept domestic animals. One would, therefore, expect them to keep dogs, and we know that they did. But we know very little about the Bronze Age dogs, and comparatively few have been found. The position is rather different when we come to the Iron Age.

Excavations at Maiden Castle revealed the remains of a number of dogs—a few of them associated with human burials—and these have been dated to about 100–50 B.C. These remains fall, broadly speaking, into two types, both considerably larger than the Windmill Hill dog, but one very much bigger than the other. The smaller of the two, which is also much the more common, has been described by Professor Watson as a 'medium-sized, powerful, rather thick-set animal agreeing in its proportions and general character more closely with the chow than with any other breed with which I was able to compare it'. It would seem that this smaller variety was a Spitz-type—which is, indeed, what one would expect—and it would not be unreasonable to suppose that in its veins ran some of the blood of the Windmill Hill dog.

The larger type was, of course, the Mastiff, the breed which so astonished the Romans when first they came to Britain. J. H. Walsh ('Stonehenge')[1] maintained that the Mastiff is indigenous to Great Britain. It is not. The Romans were not (as he thought) astonished at seeing a new breed of dog. They already knew the Mastiff, under the name *molossus*, very well indeed—for they used it regularly in their gladiatorial shows—and they recognised these British dogs immediately for what they were, and gave them the name *Pugnaces molossi*. What did astonish them was their size and ferocity. These British Mastiffs were even larger and more powerful than the fierce fighting dogs of the gladiatorial arenas, and forthwith some were sent back to Rome for the amaze and delight of the populace. Gratius, whose *Cynegetica* was written at the very beginning of the Christian era (probably before A.D. 8), records that the fierce molossian dogs of Epirus, hitherto considered the greatest fighting dogs in the world, when pitted against the *pugnaces* from Britain were rapidly overpowered. And from that time until the end of the Roman occupation a steady supply of *Pugnaces molossi* was sent from Britain to fight in amphitheatres throughout the Empire.

That the British Mastiff was highly prized by the Romans is beyond question, but there is no truth in the story, which seems to have originated with Strutt[2] and which is constantly being repeated even to-day, that the Roman emperors maintained at Winchester an officer,

[1] *Dogs of the British Isles*, 1867.

[2] *The Sports and Pastimes of the People of England*, 1801.

The Family of Charles I. by Van Dyck.

Anne of Denmark and Her Dogs by Paul van Somer.

with the title Procurator Cynegii, whose sole duty was to select and export fighting Mastiffs. The legend is based upon a confusion between two words, *gynæcii* and *cynegii*. It is true, as Roman records prove, that there was stationed at Winchester an officer with the title Procurator Gynæcii in Britannis Ventensis. But he had nothing to do with dogs. He was the Administrator of the Imperial Weaving Works, a very important post. Had an officer been appointed to select and export Mastiffs to fight in the gladiatorial arena, his title would have been Procurator Pugnacium Molossorum.

We do not know when the Mastiff first came to Britain, but we do know that it was not present during the Bronze Age proper. The Iron Age in Britain is generally agreed to have begun about 500 B.C. But the Late Bronze Age fades almost imperceptibly into the Iron Age—there is really no clear dividing line between the two—and there were certainly men in Britain (for example, in South Wales) with a knowledge of iron, and of working with iron, well before the Hallstatt invasions. One of these itinerant smiths, sailing from western France, may have brought a Mastiff with him. More probably, it was the Hallstatt Celts who introduced the breed, for we know that the Celtic tribes of central Europe used Mastiffs in battle. It has been suggested that the Mastiff was first brought to Britain by the Phœnician merchant-venturers and exchanged, together with other commodities, for tin. We know that in Assyria in the sixth century B.C. the Mastiff was very highly regarded, and it is not a far cry from Assyria to the ports of Tyre and Sidon. But there is no evidence to back this assumption. Indeed, modern archæological opinion is that the Phœnicians never came to Cornwall. All we know for certain is that when the Romans first invaded Britain they found here Mastiffs of a very superior sort. This is historical fact. And it is the only historical fact. It is, indeed, one of the most curious aspects of the dog that, throughout the world, it has not only very little early history but that it has gathered about itself remarkably little folk-lore.

The ancient Egyptians, at a very early stage in their history, portrayed the dog. Their artists portrayed a number of different types of dogs, each obviously a distinct breed, and it is evident from the length of time covered by these representations and the remarkable consistency in type that these animals were bred with the greatest care. But they have no written history, and there is no folk-lore attached to them. It is true that one of the gods of the Egyptian mythology, Anubis, is often said to be represented by a figure with a human body and a dog's head. But Anubis of the ancient Egyptians occupied a position similar to that of Hermes of the Greeks, whose office it was to take the souls of the dead before the judge of the infernal regions. Bearing this in mind, it is evident that the head is not that of a dog but of a jackal. The dog was not worshipped in Egypt, and though Herodotus tells us that on the death of a dog the household to which it belonged went into mourning and shaved their heads, this custom was really observed at the death of a cat, for the cat was worshipped. Dogs were sometimes embalmed at death—there are examples of dog-mummies in all the large museums—but this was not the universal practice, as it appears to have been in the case of the cat. Nor can the fact that Egyptian children had model dogs as toys be regarded—as it is by some historians—as of special significance. The Egyptians were wonderfully good with animals and tamed many species which to-day we would regard as untamable, and animal toys of all sorts were as common then as they are in Britain now. The fact would seem to be that the dog was regarded as a useful animal in a country of animal-lovers, but as no more than that.

The Babylonians of the third millennium before Christ were also dog-breeders, though not in the same class as the Egyptians. We can, however, recognise at least three distinct breeds from their stone carvings. One of these is a mastiff of great bulk and a heavy head with wrinkles and dewlaps. Again there is no written history, though the dog does seem to have played some part in magic, particularly in demon magic, and we know that unwanted children were thrown into the pits as food for them. The Babylonian nobility undoubtedly looked upon the dog as a useful animal—the huge chained mastiffs were good guards—but they do not seem to have regarded them as companions. It seems probable, on the other hand, that the common folk hated the dog, fearing it for its connection with black magic and disliking it for its somewhat exotic diet. It is extremely unlikely that all the children thrown into the pits were, in fact, unwanted.

The Israelites disliked the dog. There are some thirty references to it in the Scriptures, and with two exceptions they are all derogatory. The dog was regarded as an unclean animal, and the terms 'dog' and 'dead dog' occur again and again as terms of reproach or of humility. Throughout the books of the Kings runs the thought of the dog as a foul and vile creature. We read in turn of the fate in store for this royal house and that, and we are left in no doubt as to what was considered the ultimate degradation :

> 'Him that dieth of Jeroboam in the city shall the dogs eat.' [1]

And the words of Elijah to Ahab after the murder of Naboth:

> 'In the place where the dogs licked the blood of Naboth shall dogs lick thy blood.' [2]

And the prophecy of the death of Jezebel:

> 'In the portion of Jezreel shall the dogs eat the flesh of Jezebel and the carcase of Jezebel shall be as dung upon the face of the field in the portion of Jezreel; so that they shall not say, This is Jezebel.' [3]

And, in the New Testament, Paul warns the Philippians to 'beware of dogs, beware of evil workers'.[4]

The two exceptions are to be found in Isaiah and Job. Isaiah[5] mentions the dog as a house guard:

> 'His watchmen are blind: they are all ignorant, they are all dumb dogs, they cannot bark; sleeping, lying down, loving to slumber.'

Job,[6] who had once been one of the wealthiest men of his day, owning great herds of camels and cattle and seven thousand sheep, mentions the dog as a guard for his flocks:

> 'But now they that are younger than I have me in derision, whose fathers I would have disdained to have set with the dogs of my flock.'

Neither reference is complimentary, and it is evident that in Job's eyes dogs were lowly creatures. But these two references show that, though regarded as unclean and never treated as companions, dogs were employed by the Hebrews.

In this connection attention has frequently been drawn to the book of Tobit, which has been advanced as evidence that not all Hebrews disdained the dog. But the books of the Apocrypha differ in many ways from the books of the Bible, and the book of Tobit differs in one way at least, not only from the books of the Bible, but also from all the other books of the Apocrypha. It is the only book in either collection which refers to the dog as the companion of man. The book, which has been described as a 'kind of religious novel', consists of family memoirs of

[1] 1 Kings xiv, 11.
[2] 1 Kings xxi, 19.
[3] 2 Kings ix, 36, 37.
[4] Epistle to the Philippians iii, 2.
[5] Isaiah lvi, 10.
[6] Job xxx, 1.

home life and of a journey undertaken by Tobias, the son of Tobit. Tobias, on the outward journey, is accompanied by an angel:

> 'So they went forth both, and the young man's dog with them.'

And on the way back he is accompanied by his wife:

> 'So they went their way, and the dog went after them.'

Tobit is a book of disputed authorship, disputed origin and disputed date. Though it purports to describe events prior to the fall of Nineveh (606 B.C.), it was almost certainly not written until the first century B.C. Some authorities, indeed, place it as late as the middle of the first century A.D. Again, though apparently written by a Jew, there seems to be good authority for ascribing it to a Persian source. It is at least certain that the two lines quoted could not have been writen by an Orthodox Jew.

The Assyrians, the Babylonians (after their successful revolt against Assyria) and the Persians were all dog-owning peoples, and there is a good deal of evidence to suggest that they also kept dogs as companions. In addition to the dogs kept for the royal pleasure—Assur-bani-pal, King of Assyria (668–626 B.C.), kept large kennels of Mastiffs and Salukis, and was obviously very fond of field sports, as is shown by the bas-reliefs in the British Museum—the considerable body of superstition and the one or two homely proverbs about tail-wagging and barking suggest that the common folk of these nations also had some regard for the dog. Yet there is again no written history, nor does the dog appear to have played any part in the mythology, religion or folk-lore of these peoples.

Folk-lore is important in that it is a living link with the far-distant past, providing us with clues to the early stages in human thought, to once-active beliefs, and so to customs and ways of life. The fact that there is, to all intents and purposes (but with one important exception, to which attention is drawn below), no folk-lore attached to the dog is significant, for it clearly shows that, while these ancient civilisations knew and made use of the dog, they had no particular regard for it, and did not consider it to have anything other than a utilitarian importance.

It may be objected that the dog appears more than once in the works of Homer, and that it does, therefore, play a part in Greek folk-lore. But this is to confuse folk-lore and art. Homer was an artist, a poet. He used the figures of Greek mythology, he used historical events, he used his imagination to fashion incomparable epic poems. And he brought the dog into these poems more than once: not because he thought that the dog had any supernatural significance but to point a story. It is true that he believed that dogs had the power to perceive the supernatural—at least, the dogs were able to see Athene when she appeared to Ulysses when no one else could do so—but this seems to be the only occasion on which any supernatural powers were credited to the dog by the ancient Greeks, and it certainly does not entitle the dog to a position in Greek folk-lore. In fact, all Homer's references to dogs—for example, his magnificent description of the reactions of the hound Argus to the return of Ulysses, and his description of the behaviour of the dogs of the swineherd Eumæus on the approach of Ulysses—show that he knew and understood dogs very well; but no more than that.

It has been suggested more than once that Bran, the great hound of Fingal, must be recognised as a dog of Celtic folk-lore. But the authenticity of the whole Ossianic legend, as presented to us by James Macpherson, is open to grave doubt. Dr. Johnson, who was a contemporary, described Macpherson as an impostor, and it is certainly true that, while Fingal was a legendary Celtic hero, no one seems to have heard of his hound until Macpherson presented him to us in 1761.

Similar claims have been made for Cavall, the favourite hound of King Arthur; for Hodain, the hound that is linked so strangely with the fates of Tristan and Iseult; and for Gelert, the faithful hound of Llewellyn, after whom the village of Beddgelert is named. But none of these are beings of folk-lore; around none of them have beliefs and superstitions arisen. They are characters in historical legends or creatures of a poet's imagination. The story of Gelert, for example, is one that appears in the early literature of many peoples, and probably had its origin in India at least a thousand years before Llewellyn was born. And, in this connection, it is not without interest to note that in the original the hero killed in error was a mongoose and not a dog.

It should be remembered, too, that the dogs that are mentioned in the Norse Sagas are mentioned only in those that are accounts in poetic language of historic events. The Saga of Olaf Triggvason and the Saga of the Burning of Nial, for example, in both of which dogs are mentioned explicitly and at some length, are obviously eye-witness accounts of actual events.

No, it is the cat (an animal of mysterious habits and independent character, of unpredictable thoughts and inscrutable mien, and one, moreover, enlightened in darkness) which figures in the folk-lore of almost all peoples, often, indeed usually, to the total exclusion of the dog. This is true even of the folk-lore of those northern races who early came to have some regard for the dog. It is the black cat, and not the black dog, around which superstition has centred. It was the cat, and not the dog, which played so large a part in the ancient religion of these islands, the religion which later came to be known as witchcraft. And Dick Whittington, you will remember, was advised by a cat.

The one exception to this broad truth is China. And it is noteworthy that in China—despite the fact that the Chinese attained a very high level of civilisation at a very early date—the cat does not seem to have been known as a domestic animal before the end of the first century A.D., and certainly did not become common until very much later than that. Thus in Chinese folk-lore and mythology the place of the cat is taken by the dog. It is the black dog, and not the black cat, around which superstition has centred. And dogs played a big part in religion and in medicine. Indeed, so far as medicine is concerned, they have a written history going back to at least 2000 B.C.

Naturally, therefore, dogs were very highly regarded by the Chinese from the earliest times. There is no early literature anywhere in the world so rich in material about dogs as the Chinese. And this is not, as one might expect judging by early literature elsewhere, merely a collection of folk-tales and superstitions or of improbable, or impossible, natural-history anecdotes. The early Chinese wrote objectively about their dogs. Men observed their dogs carefully and recorded their habits, and historians were careful to record new breeds or types as they appeared. Thus we know the appearance, the colour, height and weight of a Mastiff of the royal household of 500 B.C., and can give with reasonable accuracy the dates for the first appearance in China of the Saluki, the Chow-Chow, the Samoyed and the Pekingese. It is to China, too, that we must turn for the first record of a bob-tailed dog; a careful and detailed description written in 143 B.C.

It is evident that dogs were regarded most seriously on their own account by the early Chinese, and not solely because of their value as food or because of the very important part they played in medicine. There were kennel-masters and recognised dog-trainers, holding high official positions, as early as 2000 B.C. or thereabouts, men able to judge the character and quality of different dogs, and their suitability for this or that work by their manner. These men bore the title 'Chancien', and were evidently very highly skilled. We find it difficult, if not impossible, to believe that a people who habitually ate dogs (and, indeed, bred one type specifically for that purpose) could be dog-lovers. But there can be no doubt whatsoever that the early Chinese were dog-lovers in the best sense of that much-abused term. Indeed, there can be no doubt that they were pre-eminent as a dog-loving nation until about a hundred years ago.

The earliest European traveller in China, Marco Polo, was astonished at the dogs:

> 'The Emperor hath two Barons who are own brothers, one called Baian and the other Mingan; and these two are styled Chinuchi, which is as much as to say, "The Keepers of the Mastiff Dogs". Each of these brothers hath 10,000 men under his orders, each body of 10,000 being dressed alike, the one in red and the other in blue, and whenever they accompany the Lord to the chase, they wear this livery, in order to be recognised. Out of each body of 10,000 there are 2,000 men who are each in charge of one or more mastiffs, so that the whole number of these is very great. And when the Prince goes a-hunting, one of these Barons, with his 10,000 men and something like 5,000 dogs, goes towards the right, whilst the other goes towards the left with his party in like manner. They move along, all abreast of one another, so that the whole line extends over a full day's journey, and no animal can escape them. Truly it is a glorious sight to see the working of the dogs and the huntsmen on such an occasion. And as the Lord rides a-fowling across the plains, you will see these big hounds come tearing up, one pack after a bear, another pack after a stag, or some other beast, as it may hap, and running the game down now on this side and now on that, so that it is really a most delightful sport and spectacle.' [1]

And here is Marco Polo again, describing another type of dog:

> 'You see the ice and mire are so prevalent, that over this tract which lies for thirteen days' journey in a great valley between the two mountains, no horses (as I told you) can travel, nor can any wheeled carriage either. Wherefore they make sledges, which are carriages without wheels, and made so that they can run over the ice, and also over mire and mud without sinking too deep in it. Of these sledges indeed there are many in our own country, for 'tis just such that are used in winter for carrying hay and straw when there have been heavy rains and the

[1] *The Book of Marco Polo* (Sir Henry Yule's translation).

country is deep in mire. On such a sledge then they lay a bearskin on which the courier sits, and the sledge is drawn by six of those big dogs that I spoke of. The dogs have no driver but go straight for the next post-house, drawing the sledge famously over ice and mire. The keeper of the post-house, however, also gets on a sledge drawn by dogs, and guides the party by the best and shortest way. And when they arrive at the next station they find a new relay of dogs and sledges to take them on, whilst the old relay turns back; and thus they accomplish the whole journey across that region, always drawn by dogs.' [1]

More than five hundred years later an Englishman, Robert Fortune, made journeys in China and Japan. He, too, was obviously struck by the dogs, but, as a good Englishman, he refused to allow himself to be too impressed:

'I had never seen Chinese dogs hunting before, and was highly amused with their performance. They seem to have little or no scent, but they have a quick eye and a swift foot, and a wounded animal rarely gets away from them. They are clever beaters, when taught as these dogs were, and at all events make noise enough. They are not, however, to be compared for a moment to our English dogs.' [2]

In Japan he was particularly interested by the toy dogs:

'These dogs appear to be all of the same breed as the common Chinese dog, and both have probably sprung originally from the same stock. It is curious that they should have the same antipathy to foreigners as their masters. . . . As watch-dogs they are admirable, and that is almost the only use to which they are applied. Old Dutch writers inform us that these street dogs belong to no particular individual, but that they are denizens of particular streets—public property, as it were—and that they are regarded with a kind of superstitious feeling by the natives. The lap-dogs of the country are highly prized both by natives and by foreigners. They are small—some of them not more than nine or ten inches in length. They are remarkable for snub noses and sunken eyes and are certainly more curious than beautiful. They are carefully bred; they command high prices even among the Japanese; and are dwarfed, it is said, by the use of saki—a spirit to which their owners are particularly partial.' [3]

[1] *Ibid.* [2] *A Journey to the Tea Countries of China.*
[3] *A Narrative of a Journey to the Capitals of Japan and China.*

This is a very good description of the Chin Chin, which is known in England as the Japanese Spaniel. It is, of course, an equally good description of the miniature Pekingese; and it is obvious that the Chin Chin and the Pekingese spring from the same stock. Evidently in Robert Fortune's time, as is the case to-day, the Japanese had not the high regard for the dog—always with the exception of the lap-dog—possessed by the Chinese. Yet, when the Chinese, a dog-loving race, first discovered Japan, they were so impressed by the numbers of dogs that they called it 'The Dog Country'. This discovery was made in A.D. 502. The first Pekingese, a dog and a bitch, were imported into China in A.D. 618. It seems likely, therefore, that the Pekingese originated in Japan and not, as is popularly supposed, in China.

The only Oriental people—other than the Chinese—who can be said to have had (and to have, in a measure perhaps unequalled anywhere in the world) a real feeling for and understanding of the dog are the Parsees. The Parsees (who now number only about 100,000 all told) are the last remaining branch of the true Iranian race, and still adhere to the ancient religion of the Persians, which was introduced by Zarathustra about 750 B.C., and which is known as Zoroastrianism. When the Mohammedans conquered Persia in the middle of the seventh century A.D., the followers of Zarathustra, rather than give up their religion, fled to India, where for more than 1,300 years they have maintained their distinct individuality, their religion, and their love for and understanding of the dog. The basic principle of Zoroastrianism is purity, and it can be stated categorically that the Parsees are the cleanest and the tidiest people in the world; but characteristic also is the doctrine of active charity and kindness to animals. Thus the whole of one volume of the *Zend Avesta* is devoted to the dog. There are detailed instructions on their feeding and general care, and also on their breeding (and these are every whit as well considered as anything to be found in a modern book on the same subjects), and there are also details of the penalties which may be incurred for permitting harm to be done to dogs. And these, by the way, include all dogs and not merely dogs which might be considered useful, such as watch-dogs or herding-dogs. But particularly interesting is the section devoted to the character of the dog:

'He has the character of a priest.
He has the character of a warrior.
He has the character of a husbandman.

He has the character of a strolling singer.
He has the character of a thief.
He has the character of a wild beast.
He has the character of a courtesan.
He has the character of a child.

'He eats broken food, like a priest; he is grateful like a priest; he is easily satisfied, like a priest; he wants only a small piece of bread, like a priest; in these things he is like unto a priest.

'He marches in front, like a warrior; he fights for the beneficent cow, like a warrior; he goes first out of the house, like a warrior; in these things he is like unto a warrior.

'He is watchful and sleeps lightly, like a husbandman; he goes first out of the house, like a husbandman; he returns last into the house, like a husbandman; in these things he is like unto a husbandman.

'He sings like a strolling singer; he is intrusive, like a strolling singer; he is meagre, like a strolling singer; he is poor, like a strolling singer; in these things he is like unto a strolling singer.

'He likes darkness, like a thief; he prowls about in the darkness, like a thief; he is a shameless eater, like a thief; he is an unfaithful keeper, like a thief; in these things he is like unto a thief.

'He likes darkness, like a wild beast; he prowls about in darkness, like a wild beast; he is a shameless eater, like a wild beast; he is an unfaithful keeper, like a wild beast; in these things he is like unto a wild beast.

'He sings, like a courtesan; he is intrusive, like a courtesan; he walks about the roads, like a courtesan; he is poor, like a courtesan; in these things he is like unto a courtesan.

'He likes sleeping, like a child; he is apt to run away, like a child; he is full of tongue, like a child; he goes on all fours, like a child; in these things he is like unto a child.' [1]

Modern dog-lovers may not (and probably will not) like it, but there has never been a better delineation of the characteristics of the domestic dog.

The ancient Greeks, a highly civilised people, certainly had no particular regard for the dog. In all the very considerable literature that has survived, the dog is rarely mentioned and favourable references are the

[1] *The Zend Avesta, the Sacred Book of the Parsees* (James Darmesteter's translation).

exception rather than the rule. Even Homer, who undoubtedly observed dogs closely, never mentions them with affection. He used the word 'dog' as a term of contempt for cowardly and despicable men and as a term of reproach for women of easy virtue. For example, he applies it to Helen. Plato (427–348 B.C.) is often put as an exception, a Greek who loved dogs. Eric Parker,[1] for instance, says: 'If there is any ancient Greek writer of whom we can say with certainly that he owned and loved a dog, it is Plato. Only a dog-lover could have written the dialogue between Socrates and Glaucon in the second book of the *Republic*.' But this is to read the passage with the eye of a fanatic and to ignore much else that Plato wrote. There is, in fact, nothing in this dialogue to show that Plato owned a dog or loved dogs, and a good deal to show that he was not so close an observer of dogs as Homer. All it shows is that the dog suited his purpose for that particular argument. Plato was the best advocate that ever lived—for he answered his own questions. Other references in Greek literature to house-dogs are similar; the animal is brought in to point an argument and is treated impersonally. In *Wasps* by Aristophanes, for example, there is a most amusing description of the trial of the dog Labes, who is suspected of stealing some cheese. But it is not the dog that is important.

And, of course, there are a number of legends. Xanthippus, the father of Pericles, is said to have owned a dog, which swam by the side of his master's galley to Salamis, when the Athenians were forced to abandon their city. This dog was buried by his master on a promontory, which thenceforward was known as Cynossema, the Dog's Grave. Again, Alexander is said to have founded a city and named it Peritas in memory of a favourite dog of that name.

Dogs played their part in the Greek religion, too. Sacred dogs were kept in the sanctuary of Asclepius at Epidaurus, and Asclepius is occasionally represented as accompanied by a dog. These dogs were supposed to heal the sick by licking them, in the manner of the sacred serpents. But for the most part dogs were used in the Greek religion as sacrifice. They were sacrificed regularly to the gods on Olympus, and in Samothrace large numbers of dogs were killed annually in honour of the goddess Hecate. This was not done because dogs were in any way holy, but because they were cheap and plentiful.

The Greeks kept dogs to guard houses and herds, and also for hunting.

[1] *The Doglover's Week-end Book.*

In the declining years of the golden era they were also, presumably, regarded by a few as companions, for the Greek anthology contains a number of epitaphs on dogs, which shows that at least some Greeks felt affection for their dogs and mourned them when they had gone. But, on the whole, dogs were kept for their usefulness rather than for themselves, and Alcibiades' attitude was, perhaps, not so unusual as it appears to-day. Alcibiades, it will be recalled, owned a very large and unusually beautiful dog, whose chief ornament was his long feathered tail. Alcibiades caused this tail to be cut off so that (according to Plutarch) the Athenians might talk of this eccentric behaviour rather than find something worse to gossip about, which would not have been difficult in the case of Alcibiades.

Aristotle, who may be regarded as the founder of Zoology, naturally refers to the dog. His works contain a good deal of curious information about the animal and its habits and disposition, but remarkably little that is of any value. 'Animals with flashing eyes are shameless—dogs, for example' is an indication of the general level of information contained in his works about dogs. His pupil and successor, Theophrastus, is concerned mainly with dogs in connection with astrology.

Indeed, the only Greek writer to have left anything of value on dogs is Xenophon, the son of Gryllus, who was born about 430 B.C. His work on 'Hunting'—it should be remarked that modern authorities do not believe that the *Cynegeticus*, at least in the form in which it has come down to us, is by him—cannot be considered here, but must take its place in the chapter on 'The Dog in Sport', but even Xenophon, keenly interested in dogs as he was and exceptionally knowledgeable about them, does not seem to have had any real affection for them.

The Romans also sacrificed dogs to the gods at certain times of the year—for example, at the festival of Robigalia a dog was slaughtered at the fifth milestone on the Via Claudia [1]—but never on anything like the scale that was fashionable amongst the Greeks. Indeed, the Romans valued the dog as a protector. So much so, that the figure of a dog stood between the images of the *Lares Præstites* of the state, and the images themselves were clothed in the skins of dogs, because (according to Ovid) the dog is a faithful guardian like the Lar. This is a very different attitude from that of the Greeks, and there can be no doubt that, coupled with this respect for the dog, there was also a considerable affection.

[1] W. Warde Fowler: *Roman Festivals of the Republican Period.*

There is in the British Museum, for instance, the tombstone of a hunting-dog named Margarita, which was obviously loved by its master and mistress.

One would expect from this attitude to find a more careful study of the dog and its habits than that undertaken by the Greeks, and this is in fact the case. The Romans were, for their time, very advanced in their knowledge of the dog and its uses, and this is reflected in their literature. Roman literature is filled with references to dogs, and these do not occur only in the writings of those whom one may describe as specialists. Thus, to take but one example, we find Cicero[1] writing:

> "Such fidelity of dogs in protecting what is committed to their charge, such affectionate attachment to their masters, such jealousy of strangers, such incredible acuteness of nose in following a track, such keenness in hunting—what else do they evince but that these animals were created for the use of man.'

And Ovid,[1] who certainly could not be called a specialist, was sufficiently interested to give appropriate names to thirty-seven hounds of Actæon.

But it is, of course, the specialists who are important for the canine historian. The earliest of these is Marcus Terentius Varro (116–27 B.C.), who was described by Quintillian as 'the most learned of Romans'. Varro, who was at one time an officer of the army in Spain, was a poet, a satirist, a grammarian, a jurist, a geographer, an antiquarian, a philosopher and a scientist, and the author of more than six hundred works, so it would seem that Quintillian's estimate of him was in no sense an exaggeration. His writings on dogs form part of his famous work on farming, which was not begun until his eightieth year had warned him that 'he must be packing his baggage to depart this life'. Varro was particularly interested in the training and treatment of dogs:

> 'About dogs then: there are two kinds, one for hunting connected with the wild beasts of the woods, the other trained for purposes of defence, and used by shepherds.
>
> 'In the first place you must obtain dogs of the proper age; puppies and old dogs are no good to themselves or to the sheep either and sometimes become the prey of wild beasts. They should possess a handsome shape, and be of great size, their eyes black or yellowish,

[1] *De Natura Deorum.*

with nostrils to match; the lips should be blackish or red, the upper lips neither turned up too much nor hanging down too low. The lower jaw should be short and the two teeth that spring from it on the right and on the left side should project a little, while the upper teeth should be rather straight. The incisors should be covered by the lip; the head and ears large, and the latter broad and hanging; the neck and throat thick, the parts between the joints long, the legs straight and turned out rather than in; the feet big and broad, spreading out as they walk; the toes being well separated, and the claws hard and curved. The soles be neither horny nor overhard, but rather sponge-like and soft; the body tucked in near the top of the thighs, the spine neither prominent nor curved, and the tail thick. The bark should be deep, the stretch of the jaw extensive, the colour preferably white, because they are then more easily recognised in the dark, and their appearance should be lion-like. Breeders also prefer that the bitches should have breasts with teats of equal size. One must also see that they come of a good breed....

'Be careful not to buy dogs from hunters or from butchers, for the dogs of butchers are too idle to follow the flock, while hunting dogs, if they see a hare or a stag, will chase after it instead of after the sheep. Thus the best is one that has been bought from shepherds and has been trained to follow sheep or has had no training at all. For a dog acquires a habit more quickly than other animals, and the attachment to the shepherds which results from familiar intercourse with them is stronger than that which he feels for the sheep....

'It is of importance that your dogs should be of the same blood, for when they are akin they are also the greatest protection to one another....

'A dog's food is more like a man's than a sheep's, for it feeds on scraps of meat and bones; not on grass or on leaves. You must be very careful to give them food, for if you do not, hunger will drive them to hunt for it and to desert the flock.... And you must give them barley-bread, and the bread should be well soaked in milk, for when once accustomed to such diet they are slow to desert the flock. They must not be allowed to eat the flesh of a dead sheep for fear that the good flavour might weaken their restraint. They are also given bone soup or the bones themselves after they have been broken up, for this makes their teeth stronger, and the mouth wider because of the vigour with which their jaws are extended as they eagerly enjoy the marrow. Dogs are usually fed in the daytime when they go out to the pasture, and in the evening when they come back to the stalls.

'As to breeding, this is usually arranged to commence with the beginning of spring; for it is then that they are in heat, that is, show their desire for mating. Bitches that are covered about this time of the year litter about the summer solstice, for gestation usually lasts three months. During pregnancy barley rather than wheaten bread should be given, for this will nourish them better, and they will give a greater supply of milk.

'And now we come to the rearing of the puppies: if there are many of them you should choose immediately after birth those you mean to keep and get rid of the rest. The fewer you leave the better they thrive, because they obtain an abundance of milk. Put chaff or something of a like nature for them to lie on, for the more comfortable their bed, the more easily are they reared. Puppies begin to see at twenty days old. For the first two months after birth they are not separated from their mother, but they learn gradually to do without her. . . . They are trained at first to be tied up with light leather thongs, and they are beaten if they try to gnaw them away, until they drop the habit. . . . Some people castrate them, thinking them less likely to leave the flock. Others do not because they believe that it kills their courage. . . . To prevent them from being wounded by wild beasts, collars are put on them; the collar, called "melium", is a band made of stout leather going round the neck and furnished with nails that have heads on them. Under these heads a piece of soft leather is sewn, so that the hardness of the iron may not hurt the neck of the dog. If a wolf or any other animal has been wounded by this collar, it makes all other dogs safe from him, even those who do not wear a collar.

'The number of dogs is usually fixed in proportion to the size of the flock, and in most cases it is considered proper for one dog to follow each shepherd. As to the number, however, people differ in their estimates. If the district is one in which there is an abundance of wild beasts, more dogs will be necessary, and this is the case with those who have to travel with their flocks to summer and winter quarters by long tracks through the forest. But for a flock staying at the farmhouse two are considered sufficient, one male and one female. For so they hold better to their work. For the same dog when he has a companion grows keener than before, and if one or the other fall ill, the flock need not be without a dog.'[1]

All this is obviously the fruit of long personal experience, and very sound sense at that. Much of it, indeed, is common practice among shepherds to this day. It is all very much more practical than the work of the better-known Pliny the Elder (A.D. 23–79). Gaius Plinius Secundus was born of a family of wealthy gentry at Como and educated at Rome. He served as an officer in the army, and later held procuratorships in Gaul, Africa and Syria, and was a close friend of the Emperor Vespasian. He died in the great eruption of Vesuvius. He was a man of immense industry, who slept little and had a passion for taking notes. Pliny the Elder is often quoted in modern books as the great Roman authority on dogs—presumably because his *Natural History* is so much more widely known than Varro's *De Re Rustica*—and it is, perhaps, true to say his view of dogs is the view of the ordinary educated Roman of the first century. But, for the most part, his writing is at second (or even twelfth) hand, drawn from his notes, and it is very evident, from his willingness to accept the most improbable stories, that he had not got a critical mind. After retailing stories of dogs in Rome and in other countries he makes some general remarks on dogs and their habits:

'Dogs are the only creatures that know their master, and also realise the sudden arrival of a stranger; and they alone know their names and the voice of a member of the household; they remember the route of journeys however long, and no creature except man has a longer memory. If they make a sudden fierce attack, it can be quietened by a man sitting on the ground. Experience discovers day by day many other qualities, but it is in hunting that their earnestness and sagacity are outstanding. A dog tracks and follows up footprints, dragging by its leash the hunter accompanying it on the line of its quarry; and then, when it has sighted the quarry, how silent and secret is its acknowledgment, first with its tail and then by its head. And so, even when they are worn with age, and weak and blind, they can be carried in the arms sniffing at the wind and scent and pointing with the nose at the cover....

'Dogs breed twice a year, and are capable of bearing puppies at the age of one. They carry their young sixty days. Puppies are born blind, and get their sight the more slowly the more copious the supply

[1] *De Re Rustica,* Book II.

Henrietta of Orleans by Mignard.

The Sleeping Sportsman by Metsu.

of mother's milk; but they are never blind for more than three weeks or less than one. Some people say that if a single puppy is born, it can see on the ninth day; if there are twins, they see on the tenth; and so on, each extra puppy in the litter adding a day to the delay before seeing light; and that of a first litter the bitches open their eyes first. The best puppy in the litter is the one that begins to see latest, or else the first one that the mother carries into the kennel after whelping....

'Madness in dogs is dangerous to human beings when Sirius, the dog-star, is shining, and it is then that it causes hydrophobia. So it is a wise precaution in those days to mix dung, best perhaps that of fowls, in the dog's food, or if the disease has already taken hold, hellebore. But for a bite the only cure is one which was lately revealed in an oracle, the root of the wild or dog rose. Columella states that if, forty days after being whelped, the dog's tail is docked and the end joint bitten off, the tail does not grow again and the dog is not liable to madness.' [1]

Lucius Junius Moderatus (Columella) was born at Cadiz, and wrote his *De Re Rustica* about A.D. 65. It seems very probable that his advice about the docking of dogs' tails was the origin of the senseless custom still in vogue to-day.

Pliny gives some other treatments for hydrophobia:

'And there are some again, who burn the hairs of the mad dog's tail, and place the ashes in lint and so into the wound.... And some drown some puppies of the same sex as the mad dog which has bitten, and cause the patient to eat their livers raw....[2]

And he gives plenty of other out-of-the-way information. For example:

'If a man carry a dog's tongue in his shoe under his big toe, then no dogs will bay or bark at him; or if he have about him the tail of a weasel which has been let go again as soon as the tail was cut away.' [3]

Pliny must, one feels, have been widely read by the more gullible of the criminal classes of Rome.

Another authority of the first century was Gratius, to whom reference has already been made. Little or nothing is known about him save that he

[1] *Naturalis Historia,* Book VIII. [2] *Ibid.* [3] *Ibid.*

is mentioned in a poem by Ovid and was obviously a contemporary. But he was evidently keenly interested in dogs and a serious student of them, a man in the true tradition of Varro :

'Dogs spring from many countries, and the disposition of each kind corresponds with the land of his origin. Thus the Mede dog shows great fight, though untaught, and the far-distant Celt is justly renowned.

'On the other hand, the Geloni will not fight and hate war; but they are naturally of a good scent; while the Persian is endowed with both qualities.

'There are those who prefer to breed Tartar dogs, a breed of ferocious anger, very different from those of Arcadia, which are tractable but will yet fight. The Hyrcanian (those near the Caspian) breed of dogs have all the ferocity of the Tartar and more, for they interbreed with the savage monsters of the forests.

'But the Umbrian dog will run away even from the enemies which he has himself discovered. Would that he had as much courage and tenacity in the fight as he has loyalty and sagacity of scent.

'What if you were to go to the English Channel, surging with treacherous sea, and reach as far as the Britons themselves. How small the charge if you do and are not attracted merely by deceptive looks and form (this is the sole danger about British dogs); no, when a great work is to be done and courage must be displayed, and the hazard of approaching war gives the final summons, then you would not admire even the famous Molossian hounds so much as these.

'With the British dog may be compared the clever Thessalian, that comes from Azorus or Pheræ, and the wily Acarnanian; for as the Acarnanes steal secretly into fight, so that hound comes upon its enemies without warning. But the hound sprung from Aetolian stock starts the boar he has not yet seen by his shrill bark; whether it is fear that causes his bark or an extreme eagerness and passion. And yet considering all a dog's accomplishments you would not be wise to despise that breed; for they are all marvels of speed and of quickness of scent; and there is no labour so heavy that it conquers them and makes them give up. So it would be my policy to intermingle the breeds of dogs. An Umbrian dam will give to the slower-witted Gaul a lively intelligence; the Gelonians will inherit courage from a Hyrcanian sire; and the Calydonian from a Molossian sire will lose its greatest defect, a foolish tongue. Thus do we cull something from every flower while kindly nature aids our efforts.' [1]

This again sounds like the voice of experience. To the dog-lovers and dog-breeders of the time, it was no doubt of great value. Unfortunately, with the one exception, the names mean nothing to us. Was the Persian dog a Saluki? And, if so, what was the Mede? Was the Tartar dog what we now know as the Tibetan Mastiff? If only Gratius had left us descriptions of these breeds! But he was not to know that he would be read two thousand years hence, and presumably to the crowds that frequented the gladiatorial arenas these breeds were too well known to warrant description.

Nearly two hundred years later Claudius Ælianus (Ælian of Præneste) wrote a treatise 'On the Characteristics of Animals'. As a serious work it is quite valueless, being no more than a collection of myths, many of them Egyptian in origin, and good 'after-dinner' stories, of which the following may be taken as a fair example:

'And I have been informed of a Sicilian dog that was an enemy of adulterers. The guilty wife, hearing that her husband was returning from abroad, had hidden her lover in her house and believed him to be safely concealed, for the servants too were hiding the guilt of their mistress and those at the door had been bribed, and the adulterer felt confident that everything would be all right. But it did not turn out like that at all, far from it, for the pet dog howled and scratched at the door where the adulterer was, and roused his master, who soon became aware that something was wrong, and being apprehensive, as was natural, broke in the door and caught the intruder.'

Only one other author of the classical period deserves mention here—for consideration of Arrian must be reserved for a later chapter—and that is Oppian. There were two men of this name writing at the same time (approximately A.D. 211–217) and scholars differ as to which was the author of the didactic poem on dogs and hunting. Until fairly recently it was ascribed to Oppianos of Cilicia, who is known to be the author of a long didactic poem on fish and fishing, entitled *Halieutica*, but modern scholarship is inclined to credit it to Oppianos of Apamea in Syria. Oppian, like Ælian, is writing for a wide public and devotes much space to myths and fables, but, unlike Ælian, he was evidently

[1] *Cynegetica.*

keenly interested in dogs and hunting, and is concerned to give detailed and helpful descriptions. Here he describes the perfect hunting-dog:

> 'A long, hardy body of ample proportions; a light head, with bright eyes of blue colour, sharp teeth, long mouth, short ears, long neck and broad, strong chest; fore feet the smaller, the shin-bone running in a long continuous line, broad shoulder-blades, the rows of the ribs crosswise, the loins fleshy but not fat; the tail stout and long and outstretched. Such is the hound for hares, deer and stags. Others again are ferocious and sustain the strength of the enemy, and these hunt bulls and wild boars and lions. These dogs have rather flat faces, and they show a terrible frown in the skin which overhangs the eyebrows, and they have bright eyes which gleam with fire, and all their skin is covered with shaggy hair, and they are of powerful build, with broad backs, and have great stamina though it is without speed; and their strength is incredible and unalloyed, and their courage is indomitable....
>
> 'As to feeding the whelps with a view to their work, they should not have the milk of goats or sheep or domestic dogs, but of stags or lionesses or gazelles or she-wolves. . . .
>
> 'While they are still young they should be given short names to which they can answer. And they should become accustomed early to the company of horses, and should be taught silence, for that is of great value to hunters and trackers.' [1]

These are good descriptions by a man who knew dogs and their uses in the hunting field. The first is obviously a Greyhound of some sort (though the blue eyes is rather surprising) and the second a Mastiff. But it would be interesting to know how lioness milk was obtained for a litter of puppies.

Reading Oppian's poem one gets the strong impression that he would have preferred to write a practical manual in the manner of Varro, but that the times were not propitious; that he bowed to the public taste and gave the dog-owning public what they wanted. It is significant that Varro wrote before the establishment of the Empire, and that as the Empire prospered, and more and more people owned dogs, so the works on dogs became more and more popular, dealing more and more with myth and fable and less and less with practical management.

[1] *De Venatione.*

III

THE DOG IN ART

MAN drew long before he wrote. It is often said that the earliest representations of the dog—and therefore the earliest evidence of its association with man—are to be found on the walls of caves in the Pyrenees. These wonderful rock paintings are attributed by some authorities to the late Palæolithic Age, which means that they are at least 10,000 years earlier than the most ancient monuments of Egypt and the Middle East. In some of the rock paintings of Spain there are shown hunting scenes in which bowmen are taking part, and in some of these paintings the hunters are accompanied by dogs. At least, that is what some canine historians maintain. It requires, however, the eye of the fanatic to see the dog in these rock paintings. One can honestly say no more than that they are dog-like creatures. They might be wolves; they might be jackals. And it is significant that the only recognisable portrait of a dog-like creature in all the rock paintings is undeniably the head of a wolf. Moreover, there is nothing in any of the paintings to suggest that the 'dogs' are, in fact, accompanying the hunters in the sense of working with them. It is, I think, much wiser to ignore these rock paintings, about which there can be no certainty at all, and to turn to the Assyrian, Babylonian, Egyptian and Greek sculptures and carvings of the pre-Christian era. For it is here that we find the first unquestionable representations of the dog.

The earliest representations of the dog in Egypt come from the Archaic period (4400–4000 B.C.). They are on green slate tablets, and would seem to have had some sort of ceremonial use, the purpose of which is not now known. Two types of dog are shown—a Greyhound type and a Mastiff type—and both are shown attacking wild animals. We have, therefore, two distinct types of domestic dog, faithfully portrayed by the artist, established at a very early date. And it is significant that it is these two types which are also portrayed in early Assyrian and Babylonian sculptures and carvings. On Assyrian tablets the Mastiff is described as the 'chained-up mouth-opening dog'. In other words, it was a watch-dog. But it is also clearly shown on Assyrian bas-reliefs in the British Museum as a hunting-dog (in particular it is shown hunting lions and wild horses), which indicates that between the Archaic period in Egypt and the rise of Assyria there had been a considerable advance in the domestication of the dog and in canine culture, and that the Mastiff had become a dual-purpose dog.

This advance is also shown clearly in later Egyptian monuments. By about 3000 B.C. Egyptian artists were depicting several distinct types of domestic dog. The Mastiff on the tombs of the IVth Dynasty (and this, by the way, is the first appearance of the Mastiff as a tomb decoration) has now come to resemble the huge Mastiffs of the Babylonian carvings very closely; a fact which led Birch, writing before the discovery of the 'green-slate' tablets, to the conclusion that the breed must have been imported into Egypt from the East. Strangely enough, one still occasionally finds Birch's theory being advanced by modern authorities. By 3000 B.C. Egyptian artists were drawing two quite distinct types of Greyhound; the original 'green-slate' Greyhound, and another which, as my friend the late A. Croxton Smith pointed out, resembles very closely indeed the modern Eivissenc (better known, perhaps, by his Spanish name Podenco Mallorquin) of the Balearic Isles and the North African coast. In addition, there appears on tombs of the IVth Dynasty a dog of the Spitz type. It is a very good likeness, with the tail close-curled and held to the side of the back and the ears pricked. Birch considered it to be the likeness of a typical Spitz; Ash, a great authority on canine matters, basing his opinion on the curiously straight stifles, went further and thought it the likeness of a Chow Chow. Most people would probably be content to recognise a member of the great Spitz family. Another drawing of the period shows a large hound with drop ears and rather pointed nose, an animal which shows some mastiff qualities but which is of distinctly slimmer build and has markings reminiscent of the modern Harlequin Great Dane.

Between 2000 B.C. and 800 B.C. the types depicted by the artists multiply greatly. Throughout this period the Mastiff, the Spitz and the two types of Greyhound remain constant; but there is now a third type of Greyhound with drooping ears and very thin legs, which is generally recognised to be the prototype of the modern Saluki. In addition, we now find an unmistakable Wolfhound, a dog remarkably like the modern Great Dane, and a small dog with short and sturdy legs. Leighton considered this to be a Terrier, but, since it is never shown at work, it seems much more likely that it was a toy and a household pet pure and simple. At any rate, it is at about this time that the toy dog first makes its appearance in artists' drawings and artists' models. In most of the books these toy dogs are described as 'Maltese' or as 'Pomeranians', and in a few a distinction is drawn between the two. The names are misleading, for the models do not resemble the modern Maltese or the modern Pomeranian in the least. Nor, as Lady Wentworth has clearly shown, can any distinction between the two be justified. Although Lady Wentworth herself rejects the name 'Maltese' in favour of 'Pomeranian' for these little dogs, it would be safer to say no more than that they are toy dogs of the Spitz type.

It is interesting to note that in the earliest representations by Egyptian artists, the dogs are always depicted collarless. In all the later representations, as also in the Assyrian carvings and sculptures, the dogs are collared and one may get an indication of the size and strength of the dog from the width of the collar it is wearing. On most of the models of toy dogs, too, collars are shown quite distinctly. And on the model of a Spitz or Chow Chow, which is dated about 200 B.C. and which is in the British Museum, there is a collar that appears to be highly ornamented. Presumably this was the greatly prized pet of some nobleman. Indeed, the collar may be taken as an indication of progress in domesticity and so in the relationship between man and dog.

When one comes to consider the work of the Greek artists, one finds that very much the same varieties of dogs are portrayed. The Mastiff (the mastiffs of ancient Greece are generally referred to as 'fierce Molossian dogs', but they are recognisably mastiffs nonetheless) is the Mastiff of Egypt and Assyria, such differences as there are being attributable to the different technique of the artist rather than to any actual difference in the dog. Greyhounds of all three types—the 'Green-slate' (the original) Greyhound, the Saluki and the Eivissenc—are, as one would expect, frequently depicted, but on a hydria of Athenian fabric entitled 'Departure of Warriors', which is dated to the sixth century B.C. and which is in the British Museum, there is shown a variety of greyhound with a feathered tail. The dog depicted is possibly the prototype of the modern Afghan Hound. This dog is also represented on an amphora of the same period and many times thereafter. Salukis are depicted on a wine jug of the sixth century B.C., which is in the British Museum, and, of course, on many other Greek pieces. There is, therefore, no possibility of confusion: the difference between the two dogs is marked when they are compared. The Salukis are exactly like those portrayed by Egyptian artists, but the feather-tailed greyhounds do not, so far as I am aware, feature in any work by Egyptian artists of the period. Another dog not represented in Egyptian work appears on a Greek bowl of the sixth century B.C. This is a dog of medium size and hound type with a rather pointed nose. It is shown wearing a collar. A dog of similar type, but with a blunter nose and a more pronounced 'stop', is shown on a Stamnos bowl dated to 460 B.C.

Dogs of a markedly Great Dane type are represented on the top of a hydria of Athenian fabric dated 444 B.C., which is in the British Museum. The resemblance between these dogs and those portrayed by an Egyptian artist four hundred or so years earlier is unmistakable, but the Greek dogs give an impression of 'breed' which is lacking in the Egyptian.

From about 500 B.C. onwards toy dogs are frequent decorations on Greek jugs and vases. All are of the Spitz type, and show no essential differences from the Egyptian. But on an Athenian jug of 500 B.C. one is shown jumping through a hoop. I believe that this is the first representation in art of what must, surely, be the oldest dog trick in the world.

In all this early Greek work there is a fine realism, an anatomical accuracy and a delicate nervousness of line, a tautness, which is quite magnificent. These are not merely portraits of dogs—they are portraits of particular breeds. Especially is this true of the work of the sixth and fifth centuries. To a lesser extent it is true also of the work of the fourth century B.C., although that is not so artistically pure, but from the fourth century onwards the realism gradually disappears. There are some good portraits of greyhounds on coins (the Greyhound is the favourite canine decoration on classical coins and gems, particularly on coins from Cythnus, one of the islands of the Cyclades in the Ægean), but they do not, of course—nor could one expect them to do so—approach the work on the vases and jugs of earlier periods. In fact, the realism which one finds in Greek art, even as late as the fourth century B.C., disappears altogether from Roman and Byzantine art.

So far as the dog is concerned, Roman art is most disappointing. A toy dog, again of the Spitz type, on a vase of Apulian ware dated to the third century B.C., which is in the British Museum, shows a marked Greek influence, as do all the finer pieces—and there are not many of them. Where the Greek influence is absent, the work is usually clumsy in execution and lacking in detail. There is, too, a pronounced lack of variety. We know that the Romans had hounds, but I do not myself know of any Roman work sufficiently detailed to enable one to set a type for these hounds. Nor do I know of any Roman representation of the Saluki or the 'Afghan' or the Eivissenc. The dogs most frequently depicted are mastiffs and greyhounds of the original or 'green-slate' type. It has been suggested by some authorities that some at least of the mastiffs shown in Roman work are 'Great Danes'. It may be so—presumably dogs of this type were known in Rome—but I know of no Roman work which depicts them beyond a doubt. As a matter of fact, one has to exercise considerable imagination to recognise the mastiff or the greyhound in most Roman work, let alone attempting to distinguish types. Except in the occasional examples showing Greek influence, there is no nicety of line and no anatomical accuracy. These are just crude representations of dogs. There is a sixth century A.D. mosaic from Italy in the British Museum which shows what most authorities agree is a mastiff facing a boar. The dog is not in the least like a mastiff, but it is wearing a very big collar which, I suppose, justifies the deduction. Another dog, said by some authorities to be a mastiff and by others to be a dog of Great Dane type, is depicted on a piece of Roman pavement from Withington in Gloucestershire. This dog is attacking a boar. The boar is about the same size as the dog, which is sufficient to dispose of the Great Dane theory at once—unless, of course, the artist was even worse than his work suggests. Presumably, therefore, it is intended to be a portrait of a British Mastiff. One might draw some intriguing comparisons between this dog and the Mastiff of the mosaic (and also between it and the mastiffs of Egypt and Greece) so different is it, were it not evident that no reliance whatsoever can be placed on the canine anatomical knowledge of Roman artists.

With the decline of Rome and the dawn of the Dark Ages in Europe, dog portraiture virtually died. One scene in the Bayeux Tapestry shows King Harold setting out with a hawking party accompanied by five dogs, all of which are collared. Another scene shows the King wading out to a boat. He is carrying a hawk, and he is followed by a servant carrying a dog. Many people have attempted to identify the dogs in these scenes. It is an unprofitable pursuit, for the drawings are very crude indeed. Legend has it that the designs on the tapestry were embroidered by William the Conqueror's Queen Matilda, but recent research suggests that the work was done in England to the order of Bishop Odo of Bayeux within twenty years of the events it records so vividly. It was made to record a historical adventure of great importance, and as a background to this, as atmosphere, the embroiderer was concerned to show that King Harold was fond of hawking and of dogs. He or she may well have had no idea at all what sort of dogs the King possessed. One, in the first scene, appears to be a black mastiff, but it seems very unlikely, to say the least, that such an animal would be used in the hunting field. I think that one can say no more than that the three larger dogs in this scene are intended to be hounds. The two smaller ones running in front of them are generally agreed to be terriers. They might be absolutely anything from their shapes. And it is just as likely that the artist put them in to complete the picture. Terriers are not dogs that one would normally expect to find on a hawking expedition. The dog in the second scene does not appear to be very big, but the attitude of the man carrying it suggests that it is a heavy animal. It is generally agreed to be a hound. It could as easily be a pet mongrel.

Dogs are depicted frequently in illuminated manuscripts and in heraldic devices, but they are always so highly stylised that they are no more than decorations in the ornamental motif of which they form a part. Even in medieval wood carvings the dogs are usually barely recognisable as dogs. This is strange, for wood carving in England in medieval times attained a very high stardard, and many of the animals portrayed (as, for example, the cocks and hens that decorate so many of our churches) achieve a wonderful fidelity to life. Dogs are plentiful on bench-ends, but they are rarely carefully carved and differences of breed are wholly ignored. Among the best are those at Lakenheath in Suffolk, Stevington in Bedfordshire, Stonham Aspal in Suffolk, Winthorpe in Lincolnshire and Woolpit in Suffolk; there are good bosses in Exeter Cathedral and in Sherborne Abbey, and very good misericords in Beverley Minster, in Christchurch Abbey in Hampshire (this is, perhaps, the outstanding medieval wood carving of a dog in England), at Southwold in Suffolk, in Winchester Cathedral, at Windsor and in Worcester

Cathedral. There is also a pleasant, and vigorous, representation of a dog on the font at Lostwithiel in Cornwall. Very few of the rest are worthy of a great art.

Indeed, from the point of view of the canine historian medieval art is a barren desert. It is not, in fact, until the sixteenth century that we approach again the accuracy and the beauty of the early Greek artists. The Italians, of course, were producing good artists long before the sixteenth century, and two of these—Giotto (*c.* 1266–1337) and Duccio di Buoninsegna (*c.* 1240–1340)—introduced dogs with sheep and shepherds into their religious paintings. Giotto is the better known for his famous fresco in the Arena Chapel at Padua, 'Joachim with the Shepherds'. The dog in the picture is smooth-haired and might be an ill-formed greyhound but for a strong resemblance, especially round the head, to the sheep in its charge. If it is a portrait, then it is a very bad portrait indeed. Nevertheless, it is an enormous advance on all previous medieval work. But we have to wait until the beginning of the fifteenth century, which is really the dawn of the Renaissance, for an artist with something of the keen eye for animal life which the ancient Greeks possessed. The artist is Pisanello (*c.* 1380–1456), whose 'The Vision of St. Eustace' in the National Gallery shows a remarkably accurate observation of animals and a considerable anatomical knowledge. In Pisanello's picture there are two fine greyhounds and a dog, which is obviously a hound, with a good hound head. Two small dogs in the foreground defy identification. But, since the greyhounds are evidently portraits of actual dogs and not creatures of the painter's imagination, there is no reason to suppose that small spaniel-like dogs such as these did not exist in the Italy of his day; no reason, in fact, to suppose that they are not also portraits. Compare these dogs with that in Filippino Lippi's (1406–1505) picture 'Adoration of the Magi', which is also in the National Gallery. There is here neither the accuracy nor the detail that distinguishes Pisanello's dogs. Lippi's is not a portrait. At best, it is a 'remembered' dog.

Vittore Pisano of Verona (*c.* 1389–*c.* 1455) was another close observer of animals, and a very much better draughtsman than Pisanello. He has a particular and important place in canine history, for he gives us the first portrait of a dog with a 'poodle' cut. This dog appears in a fresco together with a very fine portrait of a greyhound. It is about half the size of the Greyhound, with a shorter and squarer head, and its back and hindquarters are shaved in the manner of the modern poodle, the hair of the head, belly and tail being left untouched.

Another Italian artist who holds an important place in canine history for the same reason is Piero di Cosimo (1462–1521). In his 'Procris Dead' in the National Gallery, he gives us the first portrait of an undoubted retriever-type. This dog, and one of the three in the background, would, indeed, pass very well for a modern retriever.

Three of the greatest Italian artists of the period—Leonardo da Vinci (1452–1519), Michelangelo (1475–1564) and Raphael (1483–1520)—ignored dogs as pictorial subjects. Leonardo da Vinci, of course, has left some wonderful studies of dogs (as he has of cats), but they are sketches, the anatomical studies of a scientist rather than portraits. And I think that a study of his drawings will convince anyone that, while he had a scientist's interest in dogs, he had a real feeling for cats. Raphael was, I think, antagonistic to dogs. There is a dog, of no particular breed, in his 'The Labours of Adam and Eve'. It is fast asleep while its master works. And in his great picture, 'The Creation of Animals', there is only the head of a dog (on the extreme left of the picture) and this is not the head of any definite breed. As for Michelangelo—he, I think, actively disliked dogs. No dog appears in any of his works. There is, it is true, a drawing at Oxford of an animal crouching among flames. And it is true that Sir Sidney Colvin identified this as a Deerhound or Wolfhound. It should also be remembered that Sir Charles Robinson identified it as a dragon! I cannot help thinking that, had Michelangelo wished to draw a Deerhound or a Wolfhound, he would have produced something a little more like one than this.

With the flowering of Venetian painting came a much more realistic and material approach. Venice, it must be remembered, was a great and very wealthy merchant state. Great merchants then (as now) liked to have their portraits painted, and Venetian merchants seem to have been very fond of having their portraits painted with their favourite dogs. And the fashion soon spread. Indeed, it is apparent that sometimes the sitter insisted upon his dog being in the picture even when it did not help the composition.

Titian (1477–1576), whose real name was Tiziano Vecellio, was the sought-after portrait painter of the time, and we can learn a great deal about the fashionable dogs of Venice and elsewhere from a study of his work. Titian was a very fine craftsman with a keenly objective eye, and his paintings of dogs, which are done as meticulously as his portraits of the distinguished people who commissioned him, are excellent. The mastiff in his portrait of the Emperor Charles V is magnificent. It must have been a wonderful (though ugly) and enormous animal, for only a part of it appears on the canvas. (This, I think, is an excellent example of insistence on the part of the sitter that his dog should appear in the picture, for there can be no doubt that the mastiff in this case ruins the composition, and that must have caused Titian a good deal of distress, and Charles, in all probability, a good deal of additional expense.) Titian obviously had a fondness for large dogs. In his 'Venus and Adonis' (of which there are two versions, one in the National Gallery and the other in the Prado) there are two very large dogs, one of which—a mastiff shown in profile—is certainly a portrait. He also liked (as have so many painters since his day) to paint children in company with the largest dogs, thereby stressing the size of the dog and the delicacy of the child. But he was almost equally good with small dogs. In his famous portrait of Duke Federigo Gonzago of Mantua a shaggy little dog (at a guess, a highly intelligent and affectionate mongrel toy, but perhaps a representative of a breed that has long since died out) sits on a table beside his master and raises a paw. (Incidentally, this dog or one very like it appears also in his 'Venus with Cupid and the Organ-player'.) Titian painted a great variety of dogs, for he liked to bring them into his mythological and allegorical subjects. His hounds in the many pictures he painted around the exploits of Diana would certainly not be disgraced in competition to-day. But he is really important in canine history because he gives us the first records of red-and-white toy spaniels in pictures which he painted about 1505. In the Uffizi 'Venus' there is a red-and-white toy spaniel curled up on the bed. Another appears in his portrait of the Duchess of Urbino.

Paulo Veronese (1528–1588) was another great dog-lover; so much so, indeed, that he would even bring them into his religious pictures—sometimes in the most unlikely situations. There is, for example, a dog in 'Jesus Disputing with the Doctors', which appears to be listening much more intently than some of the doctors! Veronese, naturally, painted the mastiff—there is a good one in the Uffizi 'Esther before Ahasuerus'—but there can be no doubt that his first love was for the Saluki. The strange thing is that, though many Italian artists painted greyhounds, Paulo Veronese seems to have been the first to depict the Saluki. (There is a beautiful bas-relief in bronze by Benvenuto Cellini, but this is almost certainly later than the earliest Veronese paintings.) It may be that these noble hounds, so well known in pre-Christian Greece, were introduced into Italy only with the opening up of trade with the East by the Venetian merchants. If that was so—and it seems to be the only explanation—then there could be no more vivid illustration of the darkness of the Dark Ages in Europe. That the Saluki became very popular with the aristocracy of Venice is shown by the frequency with which Veronese introduced them into his paintings. He was much addicted to palaces with stately staircases as a setting for his subjects and to the stately Saluki as an ornament for the staircases.

Veronese portrayed many other breeds, of course, and particularly toy spaniels. In his magnificent 'Incognita' in the Prado he shows a very small red-and-white toy spaniel nestling in the lady's arms. And there are other records of the breed from his brush. It is very interesting and intriguing to compare his toy spaniels with those of Titian and Palma Vecchio. The dogs of these earlier artists have long, pointed noses, slim bodies and more or less straight tails. Veronese shows a dog with a high-domed skull, a short, compact body and a short nose. His dogs are square, the height being about the same as the length, and they carry their tails high and turned over the back. The sudden appearance of these little dogs is very puzzling. There is a strong hint of the Pekingese about them, and one cannot but wonder if a Chinese toy dog or two were imported by Venetian merchants and crossed with the local red-and-white toy spaniels.

Another most interesting type, from the historical point of view, recorded by Veronese appears in his great picture 'The Wedding Feast of Cana'. Leashed together in the centre of the picture, in front of the musicians, are two miniature greyhounds. They are definitely not puppies. Veronese evidently thought them unusual and important; he would surely not have placed them in so prominent a position had he not done so. A similar pair are shown in Antonio Moro's portrait of Philip and Mary (1552), and they, too, are placed in the centre foreground. Again, one cannot escape the conclusion that they were considered unusual and valuable. Several authorities have suggested that we have in these two pictures the first portraits of the breed we know to-day as the Italian Greyhound. In fact, the breed had been portrayed more than a hundred years earlier.

Italy has produced many famous animal painters, most of whom introduced dogs into their pictures. No useful purpose would be served by listing them all, since they painted the same breeds—usually greyhounds

—over and over again. But mention must be made of three. Federigo Zuccari (*c.* 1540–1609) in his picture 'The Emperor Frederick Barbarossa before Pope Alexander III', which is in the Doge's Palace in Venice, shows a very large, smooth-haired, spotted dog, which may well be the prototype of the modern Dalmatian; Giovanni Battista Tiepolo (1696–1770), a wonderful craftsman, in his 'The Dancing Dogs' (of which I have seen only a reproduction) shows four mongrel dogs, three of them wearing little coats, dancing to a tambourine and pipes, watched by a mixed crowd of fashionably dressed people and peasants. This, so far as I know, is the first record in paint of performing dogs. Lastly, there is Jacopo da Empoli (*c.* 1554–1640) who, in an untitled picture, shows a horribly misshapen dwarf with his master's dogs, thirteen in number. One of these resembles a Poodle and is shaved like a Poodle. There are four smooth-haired dogs of a Pug type. There is a Spaniel of the original red-and-white pointed-nose type and three of the high-domed type, a toy of the Spitz type, a mongrel which defies analysis (it resembles the high-domed Spaniel about the head but has a whip-tail), another Poodle type (which is partly obscured, so that one cannot be sure about the shaved hindquarters) and a large hound with prick ears. All are wearing ornamental, possibly jewelled, collars and three also have bows of ribbon. The picture gives a good idea of the kennel of a nobleman of the time.

Spanish artists have no very high reputation as animal painters, and are usually dismissed in a few lines, or ignored altogether, by those interested in this branch of art. The canine historian cannot afford to do so. There may be few artists and no great corpus of work, but what there is is of great importance. It is, for example, from Spanish artists that we get the first portraits of one of the most important, perhaps the most important, of all the groups of dogs—the sheepdogs. In the 'Nativity' by Luis da Vargas (1502–1568), in the cathedral at Seville, there is a sheepdog lying at the foot of the manger. If you compare this dog with a photograph of the modern Cao Serra da Estrela, the Portuguese Sheepdog, the family likeness is immediately apparent, and you may well come to the conclusion that, except perhaps in size, there has been very little change through the centuries. Francesco Collantes (1599–1656), an exceptionally brilliant painter of animals whose work is not as well known as it deserves to be, has a sheepdog of a different type in his 'The Burning Bush', which is in the Louvre. Compare this picture with a photograph of a modern Kabyle: once more the family likeness is apparent and it is difficult to escape the conclusion that there has been very little change through the centuries and that Collantes must at some time in his career have known the nomad shepherds of Morocco and their dogs pretty well.

Bartolome Esteban Murillo (1617–1682) had a fondness for toy dogs. He brings a toy spaniel into his delightful picture 'The Nativity', which is in the Louvre, and it is interesting to note that, though so much later than Veronese, this dog is not of the high-domed type. In fact, though toy spaniels appear in many of his pictures, I do not know one that portrays the high-domed type. All are closer to, but do not exactly resemble, the toy spaniels of Titian. In others of his pictures, usually those of beggars and the poorer classes (Murillo was born in the poorest Jewish quarter of Seville), he introduces small dogs that are generally described as 'terriers'. They bear not the slightest likeness to the terriers of the early Dutch masters, but they do bear a striking likeness to the modern Portuguese Podengo, especially to the small variety which is nowadays much used for rabbiting.

Especially important from the historical point of view are the paintings of Diego de Silva y Velazquez (1599–1660), one of the greatest painters that the world has ever known, and the only one around whose work no controversy has ever raged. This position, this reputation unrivalled in the world of painting, and indeed in the world of art, is the more extraordinary since it is founded upon a relatively small number of works. Velazquez, who was originally apprenticed to one of Spain's leading architects, was an official of the Spanish court. He was evidently a very efficient civil servant, for he became Inspector of Buildings (his early training standing him in good stead), and finally Marshal of the Palace, a very important and well-paid post, but one involving endless duties and leaving very little time for painting. He was, it is true, the official court painter, but he was regarded as a court official first and as a portrait painter secondarily, and it was because his court duties kept him so busy that he painted so few pictures. The leading Spanish authority has stated that there are only eighty-nine Velazquez pictures in existence, though he acknowledges that some have disappeared from the royal palaces of Spain and cannot now be traced. There are, in fact, fewer pictures to represent the forty years of Velazquez's working life than Sir Joshua Reynolds is known to have painted in a single year.

The great point about Velazquez and his work, and one which must

Mrs. Robinson (Perdita) by Gainsborough.

Nellie O'Brien by Sir Joshua Reynolds.

never be forgotten, is that he was the supreme realist. He could not paint without a model. This is not to say that he had no imagination. He had a certain quality of delicate imagination; but he never acquired a mannerism and he had no tricks of the trade. What he did was clear and simple : he put down exactly what he saw. We can be absolutely certain, therefore, that the dogs in his pictures are exact likenesses.

The Spanish court of the seventeenth century favoured the larger breeds of dog. Those that appear in Velazquez's pictures are generally described simply as 'mastiffs'. In the famous 'Las Meninas'—'The Maids of Honour'—there is an undoubted mastiff lying, half asleep, in the foreground. But if this is a mastiff, what is the dog in the portrait of Antonio the Englishman? Antonio el Inglese was one of the dwarfs in the service of the King, and his is one of the last portraits painted by Velazquez. It hangs in the Prado at Madrid, and the figure of Antonio is life size. The black-and-white bitch in the picture stands almost shoulder high to the dwarf. It is a very large dog indeed. But it is not a Mastiff. It is much more the type of a Great Dane. Another very large dog, usually described as a Mastiff, appears in the Prado portrait of the Infante Don Balthasar Carlos, the eldest son of King Philip by his first wife, the prince who died while yet a boy. This is a huge dog, lying in a characteristic pose with head on ground, while his young master (who was only six years old at the time) poses with an enormous fowling-piece. The picture suggests that the dog was the constant companion and guard of the young prince. It does not suggest that it was a Mastiff. Indeed, when compared with the two previous portraits, it is evident that this is a member of a distinct breed. I think we see here the first representation of the breed we know to-day as the St. Bernard.

A dog of quite another breed appears in the portrait of the King's younger brother, the Infante Don Fernando of Austria. The prince is shown as a sportsman carrying a gun, and the dog sits patiently by him. A similar dog appears in the two portraits of Philip himself as a sportsman. This animal is obviously a sporting, not a guard, dog. But it is not a hound, and it is certainly not an Eivissenc. It has powerful jaws and a marked 'stop', and the suggestion of width between the ears and the kindly eye give an impression of great intelligence. Although the muzzle would be a little too pointed—and perhaps also a shade too long —for modern tastes, I am convinced that we have here the first portrait of the breed we know to-day as the Labrador. We are too apt to think of

Labrador only as a cold and inhospitable coastal province of Canada. It is as well to remember that in Spanish it simply means a workman.

In the Vienna portrait of the Infante Philip Prosper, the little son of Philip IV by his second wife, there is shown a very charming toy spaniel. It is of the high-domed, short-nosed Veronese type, but there are, nevertheless, considerable differences from the high-domed and short-nosed spaniels of Venice. In them it requires very little imagination to see the Pekingese influence—indeed, one could swear that some of the little dogs in Jacopo da Empoli's picture are genuine Pekingese—but no amount of imagination will transform the dog in this Vienna portrait into a Pekingese. Velazquez's toy spaniel is what we know to-day, and what was known in England at that time, as a King Charles Spaniel.

When we come to study the painters of northern Europe, one very important point is immediately apparent. Though some of the breeds which appear in the paintings by Mediterranean artists appear also in the paintings by these northern artists—particularly mastiffs and greyhounds—the earlier northern painters portrayed breeds which were quite unknown in southern Europe until many years later.

For example, the great Flemish painter Jan van Eyck (*c.* 1385–1441), in one of his 'Hours of Turin', has included four little dogs of different breeds, and has placed them immediately in front of William of Holland. One of these little dogs is, beyond all question, a miniature greyhound. And miniature greyhounds appear in several other pictures by early Flemish and German painters. There is, for instance, a beautiful portrait of one, lying with its fore-legs crossed (a typical attitude, incidentally, of the breed to this day) in the 'Martyrdom of St. Ursula' by Hans Memlinc (1430–1494). But more than one hundred years were to elapse before a southern artist portrayed the breed. The conclusion is inescapable: the 'Italian' Greyhound (the breed has, of course, acquired the name because of its representation in Veronese's famous picture) originated in northern Europe and probably in the Low Countries.

Jan van Eyck is better known for his famous portrait in the National Gallery of Jean Arnolfini and his wife, which is dated 1434. Standing between the two is a little dog, one of the most famous dogs in the world of art and a very important animal in canine history. It is a Griffon Terrier. Here again we have a breed which was quite unknown to southern painters but which is portrayed by many of the early Flemish and German artists. Hans Memlinc, Albrecht Dürer (1471–1528), Quentin Metsys (1466–1530), Lucas Cranach (1472–1553), Hans

Holbein (1494–1543), Gerard Hoorenbault (1480–1540), all portrayed the Griffon, and some of them many times. Yet I do not know of any portrait of the Griffon painted by an Italian or Spanish artist within the next one hundred and fifty years.

This does not, of course, necessarily mean that the Griffon was unknown in southern Europe. But it does suggest that, if known, it was not favourably regarded by the nobility and the wealthy. Those southern painters who introduced dogs into their portraits did so at the command of their patrons, and we have, therefore, a very good idea of the fashionable breeds of the period. It is true that some southern painters also introduced dogs into their religious and allegorical pictures; usually, it would seem, from considerations of composition. The majority of these dogs are the fashionable breeds over again; for the rest, it is rarely possible to identify a breed. The dog, while recognisably a dog, is a creature of the painter's imagination. The exception to this generalisation is Murillo, who painted the poorer classes he knew so well, and their dogs with them. Murillo never portrayed the Griffon. It would be astonishing had he done so, for one would not expect the poorer classes of southern Spain to be familiar with the rough-haired terrier of the north.

The work of the northern portrait painters shows clearly that the fashionable breeds of the north were the fashionable breeds of the south. The dogs in Van Dyck's portrait of 'The Family of Charles I' are the dogs one would expect. But two other schools of painting grew up in the Netherlands, schools of genre painting—landscapes with figures, and small interiors—in both of which the dog was a conspicuous and common subject. This was painting of the people, not painting of the aristocracy—Dutch interiors, for example, are paintings of bourgeois and low life—and the dogs are the dogs of the common people. Among many others, Aalbert Cuyp (1620–1691), Adriaen van Ostade (1610–1685), Isaac van Ostade (1621–1649), Adrian Brouwer (1606–1638), David Teniers (1610–1694), Jan Steen (1626–1679), Gerard Terboch (1617–1681) and Pieter de Hoogh (1630–1677) introduced dogs into their pictures. And these dogs are not the prized possessions, the insignia of rank or wealth, of the socially conscious, but household pets and the dogs of the countryside and of the streets. We are shown the well-fed pet of the prosperous middle-class family, the dog of the farmer, and the mongrel cur, thin and mangy, of the back streets and the taverns. Moreover, we are shown dogs behaving like dogs: joining in the games of the children, the activities of the countryman, fighting, relieving themselves.

These painters of the Low Countries knew and loved dogs and were at pains to portray the dogginess of dogs. Their pictures are full of close, and quietly humorous, observation. And we may be quite sure that, in every case, the dog depicted is a portrait. These are not dogs of the artist's imagination. From the point of view of the canine historian these Dutch and Flemish painters are of supreme importance. Adriaen van Ostade, for example, obviously had a fondness for terriers, and was evidently himself the owner of a Griffon. Many a lovable little rough-haired terrier is to be found in his interiors, and most of them are unmistakable Griffons. But here and there in his pictures one can see some evidence of the development of a longer-legged breed of terrier. His brother, Isaac, in his landscapes gives us a cross-section of the country dogs of the time. Among them is an unmistakable Keeshond. Teniers, in one of his pictures, depicts a very long-bodied, very short-legged dog, which, if it is not an actual Dachshund, is surely the prototype. Jan Steen shows a Poodle, trimmed very much in the modern fashion, and Isaac van Ostade one, untrimmed, in the countryside. Both Adrian Brouwer and Aalbert Cuyp depict a dog which closely resembles the modern Schipperke. Among other breeds shown in pictures by these and other Netherlands artists of the period are unmistakable Pugs, a dog which closely resembles the modern Pomeranian, a medium-sized Spaniel, greyhounds and retrievers of a Labrador type, but not quite like the Labrador painted by Velazquez. The greyhounds and the retrievers are not shown as pets, but as working dogs in the company of sportsmen.

A most interesting point about the Dutch and Flemish paintings of the period is the frequency with which toy spaniels are depicted. These are of both types, but the type painted by Velazquez predominates. In Spain, in Italy and in England at this time the toy spaniel was the prized pet of the aristocracy and the very wealthy. In the Low Countries we are shown it as the household pet of the middle-class, and in one or two paintings it even appears as a tavern dog.

Early English drawings of dogs are almost unbelievably bad. There are quite a few of them, but, except for the greyhounds (and few of these are really lifelike), it is profitless to attempt accurate identification of breeds. It is not until the seventeenth century that we find dogs introduced into portraits by native painters, and even then they are few and far between and not to be compared with contemporary work by continental artists. Both William Dobson (1610–1646), known, for some inexplicable reason, as 'The English Tintoretto', and Sir Peter Lely

(1617–1680), who was the greatest English portrait painter of the seventeenth century—Sir Anthony Van Dyck was, of course, a Fleming—introduced dogs into their pictures. They were, however, merely following a convention. Two comparatively little known portrait painters, Mathew Dixon (*c.* 1640–1710) and Joseph Michael Wright (1734–1797), were much better as painters of dogs. Dixon's portrait of 'The Duke of Grafton as a Boy' shows a large and shaggy dog, which some authorities maintain is an Old English Sheepdog, sitting by his master. Wright's portrait of 'John and Randolph Corbet' shows the younger boy playing with an elaborately trimmed poodle.

The most important English painter of animals in the seventeenth century, however, was Francis Barlow (1626–1702). Barlow, best known for his pictures of birds, was the father of English sporting painting. He painted many pictures of the old slow-running Southern Hound. It is interesting to note that in one of his pictures of this breed, which is in the collection of Lord Onslow, one of the hounds is spotted. Barlow was a close observer, a keen student of anatomy and a countryman (he was born in Lincolnshire), with a countryman's knowledge of sport and natural history. His work shows clearly enough the influence of the contemporary Flemish painters, but it would be quite wrong to suggest that he copied either their methods or their mannerisms. That he learnt from them cannot be doubted, but he was very far from a copyist. There is about all his work a quality that is English to the core.

Early in the eighteenth century John Wootton (1678–1765) became famous for his pictures of horses. Wootton, who lived at Newmarket, is said on no very good authority (for we know that his artistic education was paid for by the third Duke of Beaufort) to have been the pupil of John Wyck, the Dutch painter of hunting scenes. His pictures certainly bear little trace of Dutch influence. Quite apart from his portrait of dogs, for which he received high fees, Wootton introduced dogs into many of his equestrian pictures. He was the first English painter to depict the Saluki, a breed of which he was evidently very fond, and it is interesting to note that his Salukis differ hardly at all from those painted by Veronese nearly two hundred years earlier.

Sir Joshua Reynolds (1723–1792) deliberately modelled himself on the great Italian portrait painters, and, following their example, introduced dogs into many of his pictures. More often than not, as in his 'Lady Betty Delme and Children', the dog is included solely to complete the composition. But in at least two of his portraits we have also careful portraits of dogs. In his portrait of 'Charles William Henry, Earl of Dalkeith' there is included a black Cocker Spaniel; and this, I believe, is the first portrait of a black Cocker. In his portrait of 'Nelly O'Brien' in the Wallace Collection—he painted this fascinating lady, who was the leading courtesan of her time, on several occasions—a small white dog lies on the lady's lap. This is, beyond question, a Maltese; and again this, I believe, is the first English portrait of the breed.

Thomas Gainsborough (1727–1788) was a much more gifted painter than Reynolds. Especially in his early portraits—those he painted before he left Suffolk—he delighted to include dogs, and each is a faithful portrait. Gainsborough, indeed, has given us better portraits of Setters and Collies than have any of the acknowledged animal painters of the period. In his famous portrait of Mrs. Robinson as 'Perdita', a dog—which has been variously described as a Samoyed, as a Keeshond and as a Pomeranian—sits by the side of the actress. A very similar animal is portrayed in his 'White Dogs : Pomeranian Bitch and Puppy', which is in the Tate Gallery. The bitch is undoubtedly a Spitz. Presumably it was known as a Pomeranian in Gainsborough's day. These pictures are very interesting, for they show what the breed was like before the 'Fancy' set to work on it.

One other portrait painter must be mentioned on the strength of a single picture. This is Francis Wheatley (1747–1801), of 'Cries of London' fame. And the picture is his portrait of the second Duke of Newcastle. In this picture there are five dogs, three of them Clumber Spaniels. These three are almost certainly descendants of the first Clumbers to be imported.

Two other artists, who were not specifically animal painters, but who have left us better pictures of dogs than have the vast majority of the animal painters proper, must also be mentioned. They are William Hogarth (1697–1764) and Thomas Rowlandson (1756–1827). Hogarth introduced dogs into a number of his paintings, notably 'A Family Group', 'Fishing Party' and 'David Garrick in the Green Room'. A pug and a small mongrel Spaniel appear in 'A Rake's Progress', and in the savagely satirical 'Marriage à la Mode' two dogs are coupled. But his most famous dog portrait appears in his self-portrait. This is his own faithful and much loved Trump, who is buried in the garden of his master's house at Chiswick. The art critics usually describe Trump as a Pug. But Hogarth painted Pugs—notably in 'A Rake's Progress'—and Trump is obviously not a Pug. Clifford Hubbard is of the opinion that he was a mongrel with some smooth-coated terrier in him. It may be that he was a cross between a Pug and a Bulldog. He was certainly not, judging by Hogarth's other pictures, a pure Pug.

Rowlandson was a great lover of dogs and never lost an opportunity of introducing one into his drawings and caricatures. It may be said that his dogs are also caricatures, and there is certainly some exaggeration in most of them, but they are, nevertheless, every whit as true to life as are his caricatures of men and women—and no man saw mankind more clearly than Thomas Rowlandson. For the student of breeds and their history Rowlandson's work is valueless; for the man who appreciates a mongrel they are without compare.

The eighteenth century and the first half of the nineteenth century was a period prolific in animal painters. There are, indeed, far too many to list. The most important are: James Seymour (1702–1752), George Stubbs (1724–1806), Sawrey Gilpin (1733–1807), Francis Sartorious (1734–1804), Philip Reinagle (1749–1833), Thomas Bewick (1753–1828), George Morland (1763–1804), Ben Marshall (1767–1835), James Ward (1769–1859), John Ferneley (1782–1860), Henry Alken (1785–1841), Abraham Cooper (1787–1868), John Frederick Herring (1793–1865) and Sir Edwin Landseer (1802–1873), all of whom painted dogs.

George Stubbs is usually thought of only as a painter of horses, and it is true that as a painter of horses he has never been equalled by an English artist. Stubbs, however, painted many other animals—there is, for example, a wonderful portrait of a rhinoceros in the Hunterian Collection at the Royal College of Surgeons—and among them many dogs. Dogs appear in some of his equestrian studies, but he also painted many portraits of individual dogs. Especially worthy of close attention are his portraits of a Foxhound, a Bull Terrier and a Land Spaniel. His Foxhound would be highly commended, if no more, at Peterborough to-day.

Philip Reinagle, who started as a portrait painter, also painted many Spaniels. He made a special study of 'Springing Spaniels' and Setters, and it is interesting to compare the conformation of his Springing Spaniels with that of Stubbs' Land Spaniel. But perhaps the most interesting of all Reinagle's dog portraits is his oil-painting of an Old English Sheepdog. The student of breeds has much to ponder here.

George Morland is famous for his pictures of horses and pigs, but he was equally good with dogs and, towards the end of his life, loved to include them in his country scenes. On the evidence of his pictures, he was particularly fond of Bull Terriers and Setters. Ben Marshall, too, is famous for his horses, but was equally good with dogs and, particularly, with Foxhounds. The hounds in his 'William Fermor and his Hounds at Tusmore' would do credit to any modern pack. Marshall was himself a keen shooting-man, and owned a couple of pointers whose portraits he painted. But his favourite dog (which appears in his self-portrait) was a large Newfoundland. This is an excellent portrait of a dog, and here again the student of breeds has much to ponder.

James Ward, who was the brother-in-law of George Morland, was, perhaps, the greatest all-round animal painter that Britain has produced. His fees were high—it is said that at his peak he was earning fifty guineas a day—and his output was enormous. He painted a number of Masters of Foxhounds surrounded by their packs, and these pictures give the impression that each hound is an individual portrait. But Ward's love, I think, was the Greyhound. There are two really beautiful Greyhounds in his 'Coursing in Sussex', and his 'Persian Greyhounds' is a wonderfully fine portrait of Salukis.

The Alken family, Danish by origin, span the period 1756 (when Samuel Alken was born) to 1894 (when Henry Gordon Alken died). The most important of them was Henry Alken senior, a very fine draughtsman with a passionate love of hounds and sport of all kinds. His hounds, however, are certainly no better than those of many another animal painter of the time—it is rather the liveliness of his work which gives it distinction—and his importance for the historian lies in his paintings of the forgotten sports, bull-baiting, bear-baiting and so forth. Here we see the true fighting Bull Terrier in action.

John Frederick Herring, a member of a Dutch family but born in England, was a pupil of Abraham Cooper, whose 'Crib and Rosa' is surely the best of all bulldog portraits. Herring painted many a pack of foxhounds (adhering to the old convention of making them run with all their legs outstretched), and many heads of sporting dogs. His full-length portrait of 'Judge', a famous greyhound of the day, must take high rank among the greyhound portraits of all time.

I suppose that of all English dog painters, Sir Edwin Landseer is the best known to the man in the street. It is fashionable nowadays to sneer at Landseer for his sentimentality. It is true that he painted dogs dressed up as human beings, that he built sentimental stories around his dog portraits, that he gave far too many of his pictures sentimental, and often ridiculous titles—as, for example, 'A Distinguished Member of the Humane Society', which shows a black-and-white Newfoundland lying on a jetty, apparently waiting for someone to save; and 'Saved', which shows the same dog after saving a child from drowning—but all this amounts to is that Landseer knew his public, and was a good business-man. His sentimentality brought him wealth, immense popularity and the friendship of the Royal Family. Apart from this, Landseer was a superb craftsman, and he had a vast knowledge of, and love for, dogs. And there is, among his work, some of the best dog portraiture that has ever been done. His Deerhound 'Hafed' is superb, and there has, surely, never been a better portrait of King Charles and Blenheim Spaniels than that to be seen in the Tate Gallery.

There are few 'new' breeds to be seen in the work of these artists. Their importance lies in the opportunities which they give for comparison as between the breed then and now. It is no less an education to compare the dogs of some of the recent moderns—Maud Earl, Arthur Wardle, R. Ward Binks, G. Vernon-Stokes, for instance—with those of contemporary artists.

IV

THE DOG IN LITERATURE

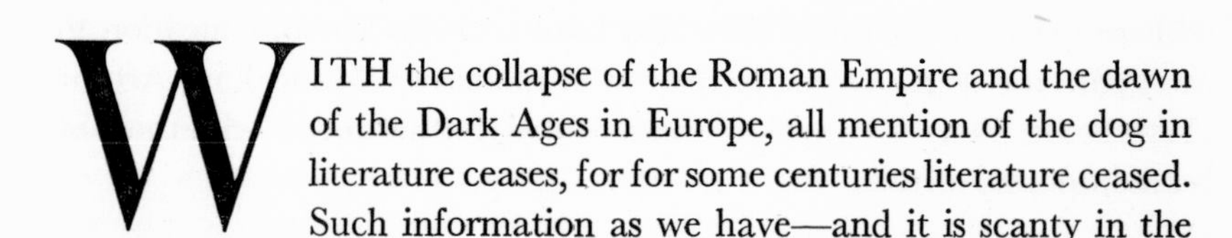

WITH the collapse of the Roman Empire and the dawn of the Dark Ages in Europe, all mention of the dog in literature ceases, for for some centuries literature ceased. Such information as we have—and it is scanty in the extreme—is derived solely from a study of the laws passed by early British monarchs. Thus, among the laws of Alfred the Great we find :

> 'Of tearing by a Dog. If a dog tear or bite a man, for the first misdeed let vi shillings be paid, if he give him food; for the second time xii shillings; for the third xxx shillings. If, after any of these misdeeds, the dog escapes, let this bot nevertheless take place. If the dog do more misdeeds, and he keep him, let him bot according to the full wer as well as for wound-bot, as for whatever he may do.'

From this it is apparent that the feeding of a dog was taken to constitute ownership. A 'bot' is, of course, compensation. 'The full wer' is the full price to be paid for a man killed. These are very heavy fines. Evidently, the dogs of Alfred's day retained much of the ferocity that had made British dogs so popular in the gladiatorial arenas of Rome.

Almost a century later we find this among the laws of Edgar: 'An oxe's bell and a dog's collar and a blast horn, either of these three shall be worth a shilling, and each is reckoned an informer.' The dog's collar was known as a 'melda' (melda means informer), and it seems likely that this was because it had a bell attached to it. These collars were the broad leather bands studded with nails described by Varro—they survive to this day in the form of the brass-studded collar—and were designed (as with the Romans) not as a means of control but as a protection for the throat against attack by wild beasts. The collars of dogs belonging to the nobility were often richly ornamented with scrolls, the decoration varying with each family, and details of these were recorded in a register.

Two years or so after Edgar ascended the throne of England (*c.* 943), Hywel Dda (Howell the Good), Prince of Wales, promulgated his famous laws.[1] Included in these is a list of the different sorts of dogs to be found in Wales—the first detailed classification to be made anywhere in the world—and their values. Among these dogs were: the gellgi (buckhound), colwyn (at this distance of time we have no means of identifying this breed: colwyn is translated by Ash[2] as 'spaniel', but the Welsh for spaniel is adargi, and, in any case, there were certainly no spaniels in Wales in the tenth century), milgi (greyhound), orlhain (tracker), bytheuad (hound), bugeilgi (shepherd-dog), gwalgi (watchdog) and ci taeog (peasant dog).

The values placed on some of these dogs are interesting. A royal buckhound was valued at one pound when trained—and that is the same value as was placed on a stallion—but, untrained, the value was only six score pence. There was an ascending scale: fifteen pence from birth to the opening of the eyes, thirty pence when a whelp, and three score pence when a year old.

Astonishingly enough, a colwyn was held to be of the same value as a royal buckhound, and a colwyn owned by a noble family was valued at the same price. The colwyn, incidentally, seems to have been owned only by royalty and members of the nobility. Now, colwyn means 'crab' or 'bantling', which suggests that it was a small animal. Certainly it was highly prized. The inescapable conclusion is that it was a lap-dog and that there were not many of them.

The value of a greyhound, at all stages of its life, was just half that of a royal buckhound. A good shepherd-dog attained the same value as a trained greyhound—that is, six score pence. A peasant dog, on the other hand, was valued at only fourpence.

Hywel Dda did not legislate against poaching; nor did the Saxon kings of England. The Welsh princes and the Welsh nobility, and the Saxon kings and lords, were much addicted to hunting, and there can be no doubt that the ordinary folk of tenth-century Wales and Saxon

[1] Aneurin Owen: *Ancient Laws and Institutes of Wales.*
[2] *Dogs: Their History and Development.*

England poached game whenever they had the opportunity. When caught, no doubt they were punished and punished severely, but the privileged of the time evidently did not consider it necessary to have special laws to protect their interests, and there does not seem to have been any restriction on the keeping of dogs by the peasantry.

The situation was very different under the Danish kings. Canute came to the throne in 1016, and in that year, at the Parliament held at Winchester, he passed a number of laws designed to prevent poaching and to protect game. The penalties were severe. Death was the price to be paid for hunting on Crown lands. To take a stag outside Crown lands was punishable by flogging and two years' imprisonment, and for a second offence the punishment was outlawry.

The Normans, who had a passion for hunting, made these laws very much more severe and enforced them rigorously. Death remained the penalty for taking a stag, buck or hind on Crown lands, but under William I the man caught taking a deer elsewhere did not suffer flogging and imprisonment—he had his eyes put out. And now there were imposed severe restrictions on the keeping of dogs on forest lands.[1] Only dogs small enough to pass through an iron ring seven inches in diameter, and shepherd-dogs, could be kept on forest lands without mutilation; and should a shepherd-dog be found chasing game the fine imposed on its owner was sufficient to beggar the family. All other dogs had to be hamstrung—the operation was then known as 'hambling'; that is, the great tendon at the knee on the hind legs was cut. Dogs so cut were crippled. That these measures failed to prevent poaching on a large and increasing scale is shown by the fact that each successive monarch imposed new and harsher penalties, and enforced them still more strictly. Finally, King John ordered that all dogs and Mastiffs in every forest throughout the country were to be destroyed.[2]

All this not only failed to stop poaching, it aroused a great deal of public unrest. In a countryside over-stocked with robbers and bandits a good guard-dog was invaluable, and a crippled dog was of little use as a guard. Apart from that, even the extremely insensitive peasant of the time, accustomed though he was to brutality, could not easily stomach the sight of a legion of crippled dogs, and there is some evidence that the men employed to perform the operation did not altogether relish it, and sometimes turned a blind eye on the dogs of the neighbourhood. At any

[1] John Manwood: *A Treatise and Discourse of the Laws of the Forest.*
[2] John Twysden: *Historiæ Anglicanæ Scriptores.*

rate, Henry II had the method of mutilation altered. No longer was the dog hamstrung; instead, the ball of the foot was cut, a deep incision being made horizontally across it. This was extremely painful to the dog, and was soon given up—not because it was painful to the dog, but because it was found almost impossible to handle a Mastiff during the operation, and a good many of the operators were severely injured by the dogs they were attemping to cut—in favour of lawing. Lawing—originally clawing—meant that three claws of the right forefoot were struck off. This could be done with one blow by an expert, and the dogs had, by law, to be taken to the expert. Lawing applied only to Mastiffs on forest lands, and not, as is so often stated, to dogs of all sorts throughout the country. Only Mastiffs, when lawed, and dogs small enough to pass through the iron ring were allowed to be kept on forest lands.[1] And Mastiffs, in point of fact, were allowed only to farmers and to gentlemen of position. King John's law still held for all other dogs on forest lands.

These various laws do not tell us very much about the kinds of dogs kept in Britain in Norman and Plantagenet times—indeed, only the Mastiff and the Greyhound can be identified with certainty, though we know that the Norman conquerors brought scenting hounds with them; and what they do tell us about the treatment of dogs does not indicate that they were held in high esteem. They had their uses—in the hunting field and as guards for homes or flocks, and as such they received some attention[2]—but they were certainly not regarded as pets or companions by the vast majority of people.

Not only in England but throughout western and central Europe, interest in hunting was paramount. The earliest works mentioning dogs to be written in Europe after the long darkness which followed the collapse of the Roman Empire are all concerned with hunting in one form or another, and in all it is apparent that it is the quarry and not the hound that is considered of the first importance.

The earliest of these works is the anonymous *La Chace du Cerf*, which was written about 1250. As a treatise on hunting, it is of some importance; as a work on hounds, it is valueless. The same may be said of Guillaume Twici's *Le Art de Venerie*, a very short work which was written about 1320 and is the earliest known treatise on hunting in Eng-

[1] W. B. Daniel: *Rural Sports*.

[2] Details of the feeding of royal hounds may be found in the Close Rolls of King John and Henry III, in the Privy Purse Expenses of Henry VIII, and so on.

land. Twici is said to have been born near Reading in Berkshire, but he had evidently had experience as a hunt servant in France before he became huntsman to Edward II. The original manuscript[1] is planned in the form of question and answer, and is written in archaic French. Twici has very little to say about hounds, and is chiefly concerned with the conventional notes on the horn and with the cries which the huntsman should use to control his hounds. Some thirty years later (*c.* 1350; though it was not actually published until 1582), Alfonso XI, King of Castile and Leon, wrote the *Libro de la Monteria*. This is the first work in Spanish dealing with dogs, and, as might be expected from its period, it is chiefly concerned with the use of dogs in the hunting field. But Alfonso differs from his predecessors in that he had, quite apart from their value to him in his favourite pursuits, some feeling for dogs, and he does mention, though very briefly, such details as kennelling and so forth.

But the outstanding work of the fourteenth century is *Le Livre de Chasse*, written by Count Gaston de Foix, better known as Gaston Phebus, in 1387. This 'brave, violent and magnificent representative of the age of chivalry'[2] was 'distinguished all his life in arms, love and hunting'. His hunting expeditions were conducted in company with his wife Agnes, the sister of Charles the Bad, and, according to Froissart, the pair took round with them no fewer than 1,600 hounds of assorted breeds. Portions of *Le Livre de Chasse* are based on an earlier work, *Le Livre du Roy Modus et de la Royne Racio*, an anonymous work which some authorities ascribe to Count Tancarville, but most of it is undoubtedly original, containing the author's own ideas and based upon his own experiences. Gaston Phebus gives excellent descriptions of the beasts of venery and of the hounds used in their pursuit, and there are illustrations of a number of different types of hounds. But it would be idle to pretend that *Le Livre de Chasse* is in any sense a dog book; it is a treatise on the art of hunting. Despite his 1,600 hounds, Gaston de Foix does not appear to have had any real interest in dogs.

The first book on sport to be written in the English language, and the first to deal with dogs at any length, is *The Master of Game*, which was written between the years 1406 and 1413.[3] The author—Edward,

[1] A translation, edited by Sir Henry Dryden, was published in 1843.

[2] Jean Froissart: *Chronicles.*

[3] The manuscript of *The Master of Game* remained unpublished for nearly 500 years. A sumptuous edition, edited by William A. and F. Baillie-Grohman, was published by Chatto & Windus in 1904. This was limited to 600 copies, of

second Duke of York and the grandson of Edward III—held the office of 'Master of Game' to Henry IV, but he was at the time imprisoned in Pevensey Castle on a charge of plotting against the King. He dedicates his 'littel symple book' to the King's eldest son; evidently a most tactful gesture, for as soon as Henry V came to the throne he was released, only to be killed two years later on the field of Agincourt. His book consists of thirty-five short chapters, and of these thirty are an almost literal translation of *Le Livre de Chasse*. But the remaining five chapters are undoubtedly original, and give an excellent description of hunting in England in the early years of the fifteenth century. Though primarily concerned with the chase, Edward does seem to have had a rather deeper interest in dogs than that common to the nobility of the time, for, in addition to giving some information about various breeds, he discusses (very briefly) sickness, condition and kennelling. There is, however, no indication that he ever thought of a dog as a companion.

Indeed, in all this early French and English literature we find a wholly utilitarian view of the dog, an obsession with hunting. There is just a hint every now and again that ladies of noble birth may have kept lap-dogs (as, for example, in the laws of Hywel Dda), that a king or a great nobleman may occasionally have regarded a dog as more than a means of killing deer (as, for example, in one scene in the Bayeux Tapestry), but there is nothing to suggest that dogs were cared for or understood as they had been in the Roman Empire at the dawn of the Christian era.

Early literature elsewhere in Europe is equally barren, but we do know from the work of the great Dutch and Italian painters that, in these two countries at least, dogs were kept and treated as pets and companions, and not only by the nobility. There is, for example, van Eyck's early fifteenth-century portrait of the merchant Arnolfini. It is not, therefore, surprising that the first reference in literature since the collapse of the Roman Empire—a period of more than a thousand years—to the dog as a companion and a pet should come from Italy. It is contained in a letter from Theodore Gaza to Mohammed II, Sultan of Turkey, which evidently accompanied the gift of a dog.[1] Theodore Gaza was born in Thessalonica in 1400. He went to Italy in 1430 and became Professor of Greek at Ferrera shortly afterwards. As a scholar he was

which half only were for sale in the British Isles, and was priced at £30, a very considerable sum for those days. This is now a collectors' item. The second Baillie-Grohman edition is also scarce and expensive.

[1] Published in Jacques Migne's *Scripturæ sacræ cursus completus*, 1840–1845.

famous throughout the Mediterranean world. And he was evidently on terms of close friendship with the Sultan, for he ends his letter with the words 'good-bye and good luck', which is scarcely the manner in which one would expect to find a Professor of Greek taking leave of the ruthless conqueror of Constantinople and the Balkans. Mohammed II was definitely not the sort of man with whom to take liberties, even in a letter.

Theodore Gaza's present to this man of blood was not a hunting hound of any sort, nor yet a Mastiff or guard-dog of any sort—Mohammed would, of course, have had plenty of dogs of those types, and could have got as many more as he pleased without the least difficulty—but a 'pretty little specimen'. The letter accompanying his gift, though beautifully written and filled with classical allusions concerning dogs, tell us nothing at all about this particular dog. We do not know the breed; all we know is that it was small and pretty. But, from the very lack of information, we can guess firstly that it was uncommon at the time and unknown in Mohammed's territories, and, secondly, that it was sent in response to a request from the Sultan, who already knew all about it. Gaza, in his letter, is concerned only to stress some aspects of canine character which were overlooked at the time :

> 'I would ask, who does not know how gentle and affectionate he is by nature also? For when his master is at home, he remains at home; and when he goes out, the dog goes out with him, and neither the length of a journey, nor rough country, nor thirst, nor storm, nor heat will deter him from following his master everywhere. And while he follows, he sometimes runs forward, and sometimes runs back to his master, and at other times plays about and wags his tail and does everything he can to sport pleasantly with him. If his master calls him, he approaches; and if he threatens him, cowers to the ground; and if he strikes him, shows no resentment.'

This was a view of the dog which was not to become fashionable in Britain for many years to come.

It is not to be found, for example, in *The Boke of St. Albans*, which is the first sporting book to be printed in English, and which contains a good deal about dogs, though again mainly in connection with the hunting field. The first edition (1486) consists of three parts : on Hunting, Hawking and Heraldry. The second edition (1496) has a fourth part, on fishing, added. This additional part is almost certainly by Wynkyn de Worde, but the authorship of the first three parts is in dispute. It is com-

Chow Chow.

Samoyed.

Maltese.

Pekingese.

monly said to be the work of Dame Juliana Berners. The authority for this rests upon a signature at the end of the chapter on hunting, which reads 'Explicit Dam Julyans Barnes in her boke of huntyng'.[1] Dame Juliana Berners is said to have been the Prioress of Sopewell Nunnery in or about 1481. She is also said to be the daughter of Sir James Berners and the sister of the first Lord Berners. There is no record of a Prioress of Sopewell Nunnery of this name, or, for that matter, of any name even faintly resembling it. The first Lord Berners did not have a sister, and Sir James Berners was beheaded in 1388 for plotting against Richard II, and he was then a man of middle-age. The most one can say is that a woman named Juliana Barnes may possibly have compiled the chapter on hunting in *The Boke of St. Albans.*

This hunting chapter is usually claimed, on the strength of the signature, as the original work of Juliana Barnes. The claim is, perhaps, justified in that it is set in verse : but the matter is for the most part taken from *The Master of Game.* It is to a very large extent a rhymed version of the Duke of York's book. And, I think, there can be little doubt that it was intended as a school book, a work of instruction to be learned by boys; probably, since it is in verse, to be learned by heart. There are full descriptions of the beasts of venery, full instructions about the management and feeding of hounds, and the methods of hunting, and, of course, the famous description of a Greyhound :

> A greyhounde should be headed lyke a snake,
> And neckyd lyke a drake,
> Fotyd lyke a cat,
> Tayled lyke a ratte,
> Syded lyke a teme,
> And chyned lyke a bream,
> The fyrste yere he must lerne to fede,
> The seconde yere to feld him lede.
> The thyrde yere he is felow lyke.
> The fourth yere there is none syke.
> The fifth yere he is good ynough.
> The syxth yere he shall hold the plough,
> The seventh yere he will avaylle
> Grete bytches for assayle.

[1] Facsimile edition, 1881; folio f. 1111.

But when he is come to the ninth yere
Have him then to the tannere.
For the best hounde that ever bytch had
At the ninth yere is full bad.

And there is also the following list of dogs:

'This be the namys of houndes. First ther is a Grehownd, a Bastard, a Mengrell, a Mastyfe, a Lemor, a Spanyell. Rachys. Kennettys. Teroures. Bocheris houndes. Myddyng dogges. Tryndeltayles. And Prikherid curris. And smale ladies popis that beere a Way the flees.'

Some of these breeds are not identifiable; some probably no longer exist. But we know the Greyhound, the Mastiff, the Spaniel and the Terrier. The terriers may well have been the little terriers of the Low Countries, such as van Eyck portrayed. The spaniels would have resembled what we know to-day as setters more closely than modern spaniels, and would have been in England for some considerable time.[1] The 'Prikherid Curris' (prick-eared curs) were shepherd-dogs, and it has been suggested that the 'tryndeltayles' were long-tailed sheepdogs, perhaps the ancestors of the modern Welsh Collie. But the really interesting item in Juliana Barnes' list is the 'smale ladies popis', for this is the first definite reference in English literature to toy dogs. These were almost certainly—there can surely be very little doubt about it—the toy spaniels which were so very popular at the Spanish court and among the aristocracy in Italy.

The list given by Juliana Barnes, scanty as it is, remained the only information about dogs printed in English until 1576, when Abraham Fleming published his 'translation' of the work of Dr. Caius. Dr. Johannes Caius (John Keys or Kays), the second founder of the Caius

[1] The word spaniel means 'of Spain', 'a Spanish dog'. It is not generally realised how very close was the connection between Spain and England during Plantagenet times. Ferdinand III (St. Ferdinand), King of Castile and Leon 1217–1252, was the grandson of Henry II, King of England. Ferdinand's daughter, Eleanor of Castile, was the Queen of Edward I. She was the Queen who presented the infant Prince of Wales to the Welsh chieftains from the walls of Cærnarvon Castle, and it was when she died that Edward ordered the chain of funeral crosses that end at Charing Cross to be erected. The Black Prince (1330–1376), it will be remembered, fought a campaign in Spain in defence of the rights of his great-grandmother's family. So close a connection over so many years must have seen the importation of many of the dogs so highly regarded by Spanish noble families.

(later Gonville and Caius) College, Cambridge, was physician successively to Edward VI,[1] Queen Mary and Queen Elizabeth, an achievement which suggests that he was as expert in politics as he was in medicine. He was also the friend of the great Swiss scholar and naturalist, Conrad Gesner, the author of the *Historiæ Animalium*, a work which formed the basis of all natural histories for at least the next two hundred years. Gesner, in order to make his book as complete as possible, wrote to Caius for information about British dogs. Caius supplied this in the form of a letter, which Gesner found inaccurate and incomplete, and therefore did not use. He must have told Caius why it was not to be used, for later the Cambridge man sent him the long descriptive treatise, which Gesner used, and which was later (1570) published as a separate book in London under the title *De Canibus Britannicis*.

Dr. Caius supplied Gesner with a classification of British dogs, the first serious attempt at the classification of the domestic dog to be made and one which was to stand without modification until Linnæus (1707–1778) published his famous classification of the animal world. Summarised,[2] Caius' classification was in three broad divisions: (1) High-bred, (2) Country and (3) Mongrel. In division (1) he placed all hunting-dogs, which he divided into two categories: (*a*) those dogs that hunt wild beasts, which he called the Beast Class, and (*b*) those that catch birds, which he called the Bird Class. In class (*a*) he lists Harriers, Terriers, Bloodhounds, Gazehounds, Greyhounds, Lyemmers, Tumblers and Stealers. In class (*b*) he places the Spaniels, of which he recognises two kinds—*index* or setters, and aquaticus or spaniels. (It is interesting, by the way, to note that he states specifically that the spaniel was brought from Spain, and that the experts of his time called the breed Hispanioli.) As a sort of afterthought, he adds to the list of 'High-bred' the Maltese, stating that it is a small dog much favoured by ladies. The fact that he adds the Maltese as an afterthought suggests that the breed was then new or comparatively new in Britain.

In division (2) he lists some eleven breeds (the text is not clear and

[1] Another English doctor, Edward Wotton, published a natural history, *De Differentiis Animalium*, in Paris in 1552 and dedicated it to Edward VI. This book is no more than a digest of earlier works, including classical authors, but includes a careful description of the breeding habits of the domestic dog expressed in quite remarkably blunt language; blunt even for the sixteenth century.

[2] A translation of the letter is given by Ash in *Dogs: Their History and Development*, Vol. I.

some authorities believe that he intended only nine—two of the names being alternatives—while one has suggested that he really intended only four, all the other names being alternatives) of which he says that only two are truly deserving of mention. These two are the Shepherd-dog and the Mastiff. The other names do not matter, since it is now quite impossible to identify any of the breeds he lists. But it is, perhaps, worthy of note that he mentions the 'Butcher's Dog'; presumably this is the same breed as Juliana Barnes's 'Bocheris hounde'.

The Reverend Abraham Fleming was private chaplain to the Countess of Nottingham and later Rector of St. Pancras, Soper Lane, London. His translation of Dr. Caius' work (which was, of course, written in Latin) is a translation in name only. A kindly critic has suggested that it should be regarded as an 'interpretation', but even this is too generous. The fact is that Fleming used Caius as a vehicle for his own ideas, building upon a scholarly foundation an original and quite remarkably inaccurate book of his own. The public seem to have realised this at once, for, though Caius' Latin work was reprinted many times, Fleming's English version was not reprinted until 1880. Indeed, the only parts of Fleming's work worthy of remembrance are his dedication to Andrew Perne (he calls him E. Perne!), Dean of Ely, who (he says) shone on him 'as a ruddy star', and his brilliant introduction 'to the well-disposed Reader':

> 'As every manifest effect proceedeth fro som certain cause, so the penning of this present abridgement (gentle and courteous Reader) issued from a special occasion. For *Conradus Gesnerus*, a man whiles he lived, of incomparable knowledge, and manyfold experience, being never satisfied with the sweet sappe of understanding requested *Johannes Caius* a profound clarke and a ravenous devourer of learning (to his praise be it spoke though the language be somewhat homely) to write a breviary, a short treatise of such dogges as were ingendred within the borders of England: To the contentation of whose mind and the utter accomplishment of whose desire, Caius spared no study, (for the acquaintance which was betweene them, as it was confirmed by continuance, and established by unfainedness, so it was seated with vertue and honesty) withdrew himself from no labour, repined at no paines, forsooke no travaile, refused no indeavour, finally pretermitted no opportunity of circumstance which seemed pertinent and requisite to the performance of this little libell. In the

whole discourse whereof, the booke to consider the substance, being but a phamphlet or skantling, the argument not so fyne and affected, and yet the doctrine very profitable and necessarye, he useth such a smoothe and comely style, and tyeth his invention to such methodical and orderly proceedings, as the elegantness and neatnesse of his Latine phrase (being pure, perfect and unmingled) maketh the matter which of it selfe is very base and clubbishe, to appeare (shall I say tolerable) nay rather commendable and effectuall. The sundry sortes of Englishe dogges he discovereth so evidently, their natures he rippeth up so apparently, their manners he openeth so manifestly, their qualities he declareth so skilfully, their proportions he paineth out so perfectly, their colours he describeth so artificially and knytteth all these in such shortnesse and brevity, that the mouth of th' adversary must needes confesse and give sentence that commendation ought to bee his rewarde, and praise his deserved pension. An ignoraunt man would never have been drawne into this opinion, to thincke that there had bene in England such variety and choise of dogges, in all respectes (not onely for name but also for qualitie) so diverse and unlike: But what cannot learning attaine? what cannot the key of knowledge open? what cannot the lampe of understanding lighten? what secretes cannot discretion detect? finally what cannot experience comprehend? what huge heapes of histories hath *Gesnerus* hourded up in volumes of large syze? Fishes in floudes, Cattell on lande, Byrdes in the ayre, how hath he lifted them by their natural differences; how closely and in how narrow a compasse hath he couched mighty and monstrous beasts, in bygnesse lyke mountaines, the bookes themselves being lesser than Molehilles. The lyfe of this man was not so great a restority of comfort, as his death was an ulcer or wound of sorrow: the loss of whom *Caius* lamented, no so much as he was his faithfull friende, as for that he was a famous Philosopher, and yet the former reason (being in very deede vehement and forceable) did stinge him with more griefe, then he peradventure was willing to disclose. And though death he counted terrible for the time, and consequently unhappy, yet *Caius* advoucheth the death of *Gesner* most blessed, luckie and fortunate, as in his Booke intituled, *De libris propriis,* appeareth. But of these two Eagles sufficient is spoken as I suppose, and yet little enough in consideraion of their dignitie and worthiness. Neverthelesse little or mickle, something or nothing, substaunce or shadow take all in good part, my meaning is by a fewe wordes to wynne credit to this worke, not so much for mine owne Englishe Translation as for the singular commendation of them, challenged of dutie and depart. Wherefore gentle Reader, I commit them to thy memorie, and their bookes to thy courteous censure. They were both learned men, and painefull practioners in their profession, so much the more therefore are their bookes worthy estimation. I would it were in me to advaunce them as I wishe, the worst (and yet both, no doubt, excellent) hath deserved a monument of immortality. Well there is no more to be added but this, that as the translatio of this booke was attemped, finished and published of goodwill (not onely to minister pleasure, as to affoord profit) so it is my desire and request that my labour therein employed may be acceptable, as I hope it shalbe to men of indifferent judgement. As for such as shall snarr and snatch at the Englishe abridgement, and teare the Translatour, being absent with the teeth of spightful envye, I conclude in brevity their eloquence is but currishe, if I serve them their meate with wrong sawce, ascribe it not to unskilfulness in coquery, but to ignoraunce in their diet, for as the Poet sayeth :

Non satis est ars sola coquo, seruire palato :
Namque coquus domini debet habere gulam :

It is not enough that a cooke understand,
Except his Lordes stomach he holde in his hande.

To winde up all in a watchworde I saye no more, but doe well and farewell.

His and his friendes,
Abraham Fleming." [1]

Abraham Fleming's book is of no importance, but he himself deserves to be remembered as the first of the long and very distinguished line of British sporting parsons.

During this period the publication of hunting books mentioning dogs continued on the Continent. In 1544 Michaelangelo Blondo, a doctor, published in Rome his *De Canibus et Venatione*. Blondo knew nothing whatever about hunting, and practically nothing about dogs, but this did not prevent him from dedicating his astonishing jumble of superstition, nonsense and pure invention to 'The Most Christian King of

[1] From the second edition, L. V. Gill, London, 1880.

France', nor from asserting that his book is the most accurate and the most copious yet published. It consists of eight quarto pages! There would be no point in noticing it at all were it not for the fact that author after author during the next 150 years uses material from it, especially some of Dr. Blondo's more unlikely medical prescriptions.

In 1561 there appeared another book dedicated to the King of France, Charles IX. This is *La Venerie de Jacques Fouilloux*, a most important work which became, deservedly, immensely popular. Indeed, it might be described as the first best-seller. A new edition was called for within the year, three more within the next four years, and by 1628 there had been no fewer than fifteen editions and some two score reprints. It was translated into many languages, but not into English or at least not officially. It contains vivid descriptions of stag, hare and boar hunting, and excellent descriptions of the hounds used in these sports; and there is also an interesting description of fox-digging with terriers. Not all the book was written by de Fouilloux. There are good grounds for believing that the stag-hunting portion at least may have been written by Charles IX himself.

De Fouilloux's book is additionally important in that it provided a quarry in which many English authors delved profitably. The first of these was George Turbervile. Turbervile was born about 1540, a member of a brilliant family. He was himself a scholar of Winchester and a Fellow of New College, Oxford, and became secretary to the British Ambassador in Russia. He was a very considerable linguist, no mean poet and a pioneer of the use of blank verse. His book *The Noble Art of Venerie or Hunting*[1] was described, a century later, by Richard Blome as 'stuft up with more Errors than Truths', and a modern authority has described him as 'an arch-cribber'. Blome's criticism—Blome was himself an ace compiler—could be applied with justice to every sporting book of the sixteenth and seventeenth centuries, but to describe Turbervile as an 'arch-cribber' is to do him much less than justice. It simply is not true. It is true that much of his book is an almost literal translation of de Fouilloux, and it is true that he uses material from a number of earlier authors—including Blondo; but he makes it quite clear in his introduction that the subject-matter of his book is translated or collected from 'the best approved authors'. And he does give us the first full chapter in English literature on the diseases of hounds with the appro-

[1] A facsimile edition, edited by Henry Frowde, was published by The Clarendon Press in 1908.

priate medicines for curing them. This, at least, was original work, and his medicines are much more realistic than Blondo's.

Contemporary with Turbervile were Aldrovandus, Edward Topsell and Gervase Markham. Aldrovandus, who was born at Bologna in 1522, had acquired a fortune as a merchant before turning his attention to the serious study of natural history, and was able to maintain a staff of artists to illustrate his work as it was written, and also a number of copyists whose job it was to extract material from the works of earlier authors. These men had no specialised knowledge, and we find, therefore, earlier errors being repeated and given the cloak of authority. Aldrovandus himself had no interest in dogs—there is no original material whatever in the few pages he devotes to them—and was evidently content with the work of his copyists. These men drew on Gesner and also on Fleming, but, naturally since they were Italians, they relied mainly on Blondo and the more improbable parts of Blondo impressed them particularly. One of the artists employed by Aldrovandus, however, had a real feeling for dogs. There are excellent representations of a spaniel and a Dachshund.

Edward Topsell was the perpetual curate of St. Botolph's, Aldersgate. In addition to a number of religious books and poems, he wrote two zoological works—*The Historie of Foure-footed Beastes* (1607) and *The Historie of Serpents* (1608). The former contains a fair amount of material about dogs, much of it taken from Fleming, Gesner and Wotton.[1] Topsell's value is not as an historian of dogs but as a priceless repository of folk-lore concerning them.

Gervase Markham, a Nottinghamshire country gentleman, was a scholar with a very considerable knowledge of foreign languages. After service with the army in the Netherlands, he settled down to the pursuit of country sports of which he was passionately fond. A very extravagant man, he had a marked inability to keep out of debt and, in order to keep his head above water and to continue his indulgence in sport, he turned to authorship. In a period of some thirty years he produced an enormous number of books of very variable quality, but including at least three

[1] Edward Wotton (1492–1555) was President of the Royal College of Physicians. A Fellow of Magdalen College, Oxford, he studied medicine in Italy and France, and took his medical degree at Padua. He was the first Englishman to study natural history systematically, and he acquired a European reputation when his *De Differentiis Animalium* was published in Paris in 1522. There is very little in his work relating to dogs, other than a very full description of their sexual behaviour.

classics of English sporting literature. Spread over his many works is a considerable quantity of material relating to dogs. Much of it is taken, of course, from earlier authors—notably Fleming, Caius, Wooton and de Fouilloux—but much is original and most entertaining. In *Hunger's Prevention; or the whole Arte of Fowling by Water and Land* (1621) there is this delightful description of a Poodle:

'The water Dogge is a creature of such generall use, and so frequent in use amongst us heere in England, that it is needlesse to make any large description of him: the rather since not any amongst us is so simple that he cannot say when hee seeth him. This is a Water-Dogge, or a Dogge bred for the Water: yet because in this (as in other creatures) there are other characters and Formes which pretend more excellencie, and figure a greater height of vertue than others doe: I will heere describe as neere as I can the best proportion of a perfect Water Dogge.

'First, for the colour of the best Water Dogge, all be it some which are curious in all things will ascribe more excellency to one colour than to another as the Blacks to be the best and hardest; the lyverhued swiftest in swimming, and the Pied or Spotted Dogge, quickest of scent; yet in truth it is nothing so, for all colours are alike, and so a Dogge of any of the former colours, may be excellent good Dogges, and of any may bee most notable curres, according to their first ordering and trayning; for Instruction is the liquor where-with they are seasoned, and if they be well handled at the first, they will ever smell of that discresion, and if they bee ill handled they will ever stink of that folley: for nature is a true mistresse and bestowes her guifts freely, and it is onely nature which abuseth them.

'To proceede then, your Dogge may be of any colour and yet excellent, and his hairs in generall would be long and curled, not loose and shagged; for the first showes hardnesse and ability to endure the water, the other much tendernesse, making his sport grievous; his head would be round and curled, his ears broad and hanging, his Eye full, lively and quicke, his nose very short; his lippe, Hound-like, side and rough bearded, his Chappes with a full set of strong Teeth, and the general features of his whole countenance being united together would be as Lyon-like as might be, for that shewes fierceness and goodnesse: his Necke would bee thicke and short, his Brest like the brest of a Shippe, sharpe and compact, his Shoulders broad, his fore Legs straight, his Chine square, his Buttokes rounde, his ribbes compassed, his belly gaunt, his Thyes brawny, his Cambrels crooked, his Pasterns strong and dewe clawde, and his foure feete spatious, full and round, and closed together to the cley, like a water Ducke, for they being his oars to rowe him in the water, having that shape, will carry his body away faster. And thus you have the true description of a perfect Water Dogge, as you may see following.'

Markham, it will be realised, was a common-sense country sportsman, who knew his dogs, understood the purpose for which they were to be used and was not easily misled. He has much of interest to say about the clipping or trimming of the 'Water Dogge':

'Now for the cutting or shaving him from the Navill downward, or backward, it is two wayes well to be allowed of that is, for summer hunting or for the water; because these Water Dogges naturally are ever most laden with haires on the hinder parts, nature as it were labouring to defend that part most, which is continually to bee employed in the most extremity, and because the hinder parts are ever deeper in the water than the fore parts, therefore nature hath given them the greatest armour of haires to defeet the wette and coldnesse; yet this defence in the Sommer time by the violence of the heate of the Sunne, and the greatnesse of the Dogges labour is very noysome and troublesome, and not onely maketh him sooner to faint and give over his sport, but also makes him by his overheating, more subject to take the Maungie.

'And so likewise in matter of water, it is a very heavy burthen to the Dogge and makes him swimme lesse nimbly and slower, besides the former offences before receited; But for the cutting or shaving of a Dogge all quite over, even from the Foote to the Nostrill that I utterly dislike, for it not only takes from him the generall benifits which Nature hath lent him, but also brings such a tendernesse and chilnesse over all his body, that the water in the end will grow yrksome unto him; for howsoever men may argue that keeping any creature cold will make it the better indure colde, yet we finde by true experience both in these and divers other such like things, that when Nature is thus continually kept at her uttermost ability of indurance, when any little drope more is added to that extreamity, presently she faints and grows distempered, whereas keepe Nature in her full strength and she will very hardly be conquered, and hence it shall come that you shall see an ordinary land Spaniell being lustily and well kept, will tyre 20 of these overshaven Curres in the cod water.'

All of which is remarkably sensible comment obviously based on long personal experience. Markham, who is believed to have been the first man to import an Arab stallion into this country, is also the first man to have written in any detail about the training of sporting dogs. This is what he has to say about the training to retrieve of a 'Water Dogge':

> 'Traine him to fetch whatsoever you shall throw from you, as Staves or Cudgels, Bagges, Nettes, Instruments of all kindes, and indeed anything whatsoever that is portable; then you shall use him to fetch round cogell stones, and flints, which are troublesome in a Dogges mouth, and lastly Iron, Steele, Money, and all kindes of metall, which being colde in his teeth, slippery and ill to take up, a Dogge will be loth to fetch, but you must not desist or let him taste food till he will as familiarly bring and carry them as anything else whatsoever.'

This would not, it is true, meet with the approval of modern gundog trainers. But it must be remembered that Markham was writing long before the fetish of the 'soft mouth' had become fashionable. All that he—or, indeed, any other sportsman until comparatively recent times—required was that his game should be retrieved for him. And one can have little doubt that Markham's dogs were expert in the art.

Gervase Markham was the forerunner of Nicholas Cox, whose *The Gentleman's Recreation*, first published in 1674, was to become the first 'best-seller' in English sporting literature, running through many editions in the next one hundred years.[1] Nicholas Cox was a bookseller and publisher by trade, but, living in Sussex, he had a considerable practical experience of field sports. Parts of his book are undoubtedly based on his own experience, but much of it is, as he says in his introduction, compiled from earlier books. In fact, he made very liberal use of Turbervile and Markham, and got a good deal of his natural history (including most of the errors) from Pliny. But his practical experience in the field led him to propose the use of 'a different Hound for every chase'. He was the first Englishman to do so. It was, however, many years before the practice became general.

Three years later, in 1677, there appeared the *Cynographia Curiosa.*

[1] A reprint of the 4th edition was published by The Cresset Press in 1928.

The author, Christian Francis Paullinus, was born at Eisenach in 1643 and was a physician by profession. He was evidently very interested in dogs—he had during his lifetime a considerable reputation as a naturalist—and he devotes a fair portion of his book to a discussion of various breeds (he is the first to mention the Dachshund by name) and their management. He was deeply interested in breeding, and the first man to suggest that, by careful crossing, it should be possible to manufacture a breed possessing certain desired virtues. But his main interest was in diseases and their treatment, and he discusses a number of canine diseases (especially rabies) with a down-to-earth common sense which was quite exceptional for his time, and, indeed, might have been thought advanced even two hundred years later. The book was reprinted, though there is nothing on the title page to suggest that it is a reprint, in 1685.[1]

Between 1674 and 1800 only two books of any real importance for the historian of the dog were published in England.[2] These were *The Gentleman's Recreation*, by Richard Blome, which was published in 1686, and *A General History of Quadrupeds*, by Ralph Beilby, which was first published in 1790. Both are important for their illustrations rather than for their text. Richard Blome was a publisher. His book is entirely compiled from the works of others, British and foreign, skilfully edited and very well produced. Blome published his books by subscription, and was evidently a very adroit businessman with a keen eye for wealthy clients. He could afford to spend money on illustration. Three of the plates are the work of Francis Barlow. Ralph Beilby was both engraver and publisher. One of his pupils was Thomas Bewick, whom he later took into partnership. It is Bewick's engravings which lift what would otherwise be a very pedestrian work into a class of its own.

All the works mentioned above, every author before 1800, with the sole exception of Theodore Gaza, takes a completely utilitarian view of the dog. Even in the case of Gervase Markham, who owned dogs and studied them carefully, there is never so much as a hint of affection. Pet

[1] C. L. B. Hubbard, usually the most careful and accurate of canine historians, in his *The Literature of British Dogs* says that 'this rare book was apparently unknown to Ash and Watson'. In fact, Ash mentions it in Vol. I of his *Dogs: Their History and Development,* on page 73, and gives a translation of a portion of it in the appendix to Vol. II.

[2] Buffon's *Histoire Naturelle,* published in many volumes between 1755 and 1789, has coloured plates of some breeds and makes a most convincing attempt at classification. Henry Pye's *The Sportsman's Dictionary* (1778) also attempts classification—on the basis of colour!

dogs were, as we know, kept, at least by royalty, and the nobility or by their ladies, and perhaps by other classes as well, but it is very evident that the average Englishman did not regard the dog as a pet or companion and had no particular affection for it. Indeed, it would probably be no exaggeration to say that the average Englishman of the sixteenth to eighteenth centuries, while recognising the uses of the dog, held the animal in some contempt if he did not actually dislike it.

Shakespeare, who knew everything about England and Englishmen, never mentions the dog with affection but almost always with contempt. Indeed, only once—in the famous passage in *A Midsummer Night's Dream*—does he speak of the dog without contempt, and then, in fact, he is describing not the hounds but their part in the hunt:

THESEUS: Go, one of you, find out the forester;
For now our observation is performed;
And since we have the vaward of the day,
My love shall hear the music of my hounds.
Uncouple in the western valley; let them go:
Despatch, I say, and find the forester.
We will, fair Queen, up to the mountain's top,
And mark the musical confusion
Of hounds and echo in conjunction.
HIPPOLYTA: I was with Hercules and Cadmus once,
When in a wood of Crete they bay'd the bear
With hounds of Sparta; never did I hear
Such gallant chiding; for, besides the groves,
The skies, the fountains, every region near
Seem'd all one mutual cry: I never heard
So musical a discord, such sweet thunder.
THESEUS: My hounds are bred out of the Spartan kind,
So flew'd, so sanded; and their heads are hung
With ears that sweep away the morning dew;
Crook-knee'd, and dew-lapped like Thessalian bulls;
Slow in pursuit, but match'd in mouth-like bells,
Each under each. A cry more tuneable
Was never holla'd to, nor cheered with horn,
In Crete, in Sparta, nor in Thessaly:
Judge when you hear.

Only in that one passage is the dog spoken of without contempt or open dislike. When Shakespeare mentions the spaniel, it is as a cowardly, fawning, contemptible creature; elsewhere his dogs are the dogs of the Bible, despicable creatures.

This attitude on the part of our national poet, the greatest Englishman of all time, greatly distresses the modern dog-lover. Many of them refuse to accept it as more than Shakespeare's own, purely personal, opinion —his one blind spot—maintaining it unthinkable that the views of his contemporaries could have differed from those of the modern Englishman. Eric Parker,[1] indeed, goes even further. He cannot bring himself to believe that William Shakespeare could have written about dogs in such a manner. He is willing to accept the *Midsummer Night's Dream* passage as genuine Shakespeare, but—and I quote—'would you not suppose that the Shakespeare who can write thus of Theseus's hounds would have written elsewhere in praise of other dogs? Or is it a different pen that bids avaunt to hound or spaniel, brach or lym?' And it is evident that he believes that it is.

Personally, I hold firmly to the view that William Shakespeare wrote the plays that bear his name. And I do not believe for one moment that his view of the dog was unique. We are too apt nowadays to forget that Shakespeare was a dramatist, earning his living by writing plays for the pleasure and amusement of the public. We can be quite sure that had the public of his time taken another view of the dog, held it in high esteem, then that attitude would have been reflected in his plays.

With the dawn of the nineteenth century came a change of view. There was nothing in the least sudden about this. Indeed, even as late as 1850, books in the seventeenth-century tradition were being published and found a ready sale. Of these the best known, and deservedly so, are Joseph Strutt's classic work, *The Sports and Pastimes of the People of England*,[2] the Reverend W. B. Daniel's *Rural Sports* [3] and Delabere Blaine's *Encyclopædia of Rural Sports*.[4] These are books which would have been read with as much delight and understanding by Englishmen of the seventeenth century as they were by the country gentlemen of the early nineteenth. Strutt, who died within a few months of the publication of his book, was an engraver by profession and an antiquary by inclina-

[1] *The Doglover's Week-end Book.*
[2] First published 1801. A new edition was published by Horace Cox in 1903.
[3] Published in two volumes in 1801 and 1802. No recent edition.
[4] Published in 1840, but written about 1806.

tion. He was meticulous in checking his facts, and his book is a mine of information for anyone interested in the history of sport in England. William Barker Daniel, the arch-type of English sporting parson, was not so careful, and there is much uncritical repetition of statements by earlier authors. Dogs used for hunting are dealt with in the first volume, and those used for shooting in the second. The book is entertaining but of very little value. Some of the copperplate engravings, however, are excellent.[1] Delabere Blaine had a national reputation as a veterinary surgeon in the last decade of the eighteenth century and the first of the nineteenth, particularly for his medicines for horses.[2] His *Encyclopædia* deals exhaustively, but on the whole inaccurately, with sporting dogs. Blaine, despite his profession, was obviously much more interested in sport than in dogs.

In 1800[3] came the first British dog book to be illustrated with accurate coloured plates. This was the *Cynographia Britannica*, by Sydenham Teak Edwards. Sydenham Edwards was the son of the organist and schoolmaster at Abergavenny, and was born in 1769. In addition to being an artist, he was a really good botanist. His botany brought him to the notice of William Curtis, who had him trained as an artist and then employed him to illustrate the *Botanical Magazine*. The coloured plates in the *Cynographia* were all drawn from life by Edwards and 'coloured under his immediate inspection'. It is the plates that make this book one of the most important of all British dog books. But there is a revolutionary trend in the text that should not pass unnoticed. Sydenham Edwards had no interest whatsoever in sport. His is the first British book in which the dog is regarded as worthy of attention quite apart from its role in sport. Edwards, though completely unsentimental in his attitude, was beyond doubt a dog-lover.

So also was W. Taplin, about whom we know practically nothing.[4] He was evidently a country gentleman, who from his writings lived in Sussex—it has been suggested that he was a doctor—but he owned no property and obviously regarded poaching as the proper pursuit for the unlanded gentleman. The title of Taplin's book, *The Sportsman's Cabinet* (published in two volumes 1803–1804) suggests another book in

[1] Reinagle, Stubbs and Gilpin contributed illustrations.

[2] He published the first British veterinary book, *A Domestic Treatise on the Diseases of Horses and Dogs*, in 1803.

[3] The book was issued in parts. Although 1800 is the generally accepted date of publication, two of the plates are dated as late as 1805.

[4] The *Dictionary of National Biography* ignores him.

the Nicholas Cox tradition. But the sub-title, 'or a Correct Delineation of the Various Dogs used in the Sports of the Field; including the Canine Race in general', gives a true idea of the contents. This is, in fact, a dog book, and, though verbose, a very good one with really excellent illustrations by Reinagle, Bewick, Rysbrack and Pugin. The Reinagle plates, in particular, are beyond praise. Reading the book, which contains some excellent stories about dogs, one can have no doubt that Taplin was essentially a dog-lover. In particular, I like this passage which is taken from his chapter on mastiffs:

> 'The souls of deceased bailliffs and common constables are in the bodies of setting dogs and pointers; the terriers are inhabited by trading justices: the bloodhounds were formerly a set of informers, thief takers, and false evidences; the spaniels were heretofore courtiers, hangers-on of administration and hack-journal writers, all of whom preserve their primitive qualities of fawning on their feeders, licking their hands, and snarling and snapping at all who offer to offend their masters. A former train of gamblers and blacklegs are now embodied in that particular species denominated lurchers; bulldogs and mastiffs were once butchers and drovers; grey-hounds and hounds owe their animation to country squires and foxhounds; while whistling, useless lap-dogs draw their existence from the quondam beau; macaronies and gentlemen of the tiffy, still being the playthings of the ladies, and used for their diversion. There are also a set of sad dogs derived from attornies; and puppies who were in past times attornies' clerks, shopmen to retail haberdashers, men-milliners, etc., etc. Turnspits are animated by old aldermen who still enjoy the smell of roast meat; that droning, snarling species stiled Dutch pugs have been fellows of colleges; and that faithful, useful tribe of shepherds' dogs were in days of yore, members of parliament who guarded the flock, and protected the sheep from the wolves and thieves, although indeed, of late, some have turned sheep-biters, and worried those they ought to have defended.'

In the same year (1804) as the second volume of *The Sportsman's Cabinet* was published came *The General Character of the Dog*, by Joseph Taylor. This book, which is not mentioned by Watson, Walsh, Leighton, Ash, Hubbard or any of the authorities, is most important—not because it contains anything of value; it does not—but because it is

Greyhound (Swinging Light). Winner of the Waterloo Cup 1941-2.

Greyhound (Priceless Border). Winner of the Greyhound Derby 1948.

Saluki.

Afghan Hound.

the first British book (indeed, I think the first book in any language) to treat of the dog from a purely sentimental angle, and it has fathered a positively enormous family. It had in its time sufficient success to justify a sequel, entitled *Canine Gratitude*, which was published in 1806. In 1828 Taylor produced yet a third volume, *Four-footed Friends*, which is even more sentimental in treatment than its predecessors.

From 1840 onwards there has been a steady stream of books about dogs, and one can do no more than select the most important. The first of these is, undoubtedly, Lieut.-Colonel Charles Hamilton Smith's *Dogs*, which formed part of Jardine's 'Naturalist's Library'. Smith's work was published in two volumes (1939–1840) forming volumes 18 and 19 of 'The Naturalist's Library'. The first volume deals with the wolves, jackals and wild dogs; the second with the domestic breeds. The whole forms a complete natural history of the *Canidæ*, as it was known at the time, and is lavishly illustrated with plates engraved by Lizars and coloured by hand. Smith, a regular soldier, served in the Peninsular War and fought at Waterloo. He was a careful and exact naturalist, a Fellow of the Royal Society, and his book—though inevitably out of date in many respects—still has considerable value for the student of the dog.

This was followed, in 1845, by William Youatt's *The Dog*. Youatt, who was educated for the Church, became a veterinary surgeon, and for some thirty years conducted what must have been the most prosperous practice in the country. He founded and edited the *Veterinian*, the first veterinary journal to be published in England, was lecturer in veterinary subjects at University College, and an original member of the Royal Agricultural Society. His book became a standard work and passed through many editions.

John Meyrick's *House Dogs and Sporting Dogs* (1861) deserves mention because it is the first book to deal with the show points of the various breeds and to give some hints on showing. But the next really important book was George R. Jesse's *Researches into the History of the British Dog* (1866). Gerald Massey, the leading authority on British dog books, has described it as 'an exceedingly important book, the first to deal at any length with the history of Dogs from evidence supplied by earlier records compiled by man'.[1] Jesse, founder of the Society for the Abolition of Vivisection, was a deeply sincere animal lover, but, much more important from the point of view of his book, he was also the research worker *par excellence*. Nothing was too much trouble for him. His book

[1] *A Catalogue of Dog Books*, 1945.

is a mine of information, and has been extensively used by all subsequent writers on canine history, notably by E. C. Ash. All these men have been at pains to point out and correct (not always correctly!) inaccuracies in Jesse's work—considering that it is a pioneer work there are remarkably few—but none has denied its great value.

But we have run ahead of time. Back in 1853 Longmans, Green had published *The Greyhound*, by J. H. Walsh. This was the first work on the breed (apart from Arrian's treatise) ever to be published. At the time it did not cause much of a stir, except among greyhound enthusiasts, but it gradually came to be recognised for what it is, a classic work—and many editions were called for. Even to-day, more than a century later, it can justly be regarded as a standard authority. John Henry Walsh, under his pseudonym 'Stonehenge', was to become one of the most famous names in the history of dog and sporting literature. Born in London in 1810, he qualified as a surgeon, and practised medicine, first in London and then in Worcester, for more than twenty years, during which time he wrote a number of medical books and one, which had a big sale in its day, on cookery. But his great interest was in sport, and particularly in coursing. In 1856 he was instrumental in founding *The Coursing Calendar* (a publication which has continued to this day) and became its first editor, and a year later he was appointed editor-in-chief of *The Field*. Prior to leaving medicine for journalism, he published, in 1855, *The Manual of British Rural Sports*, and undoubtedly it was this monumental work which took him at one bound to the leading position in British sporting journalism. He has left it on record that it took him twenty years, working some part of every day, to write *The Manual*, and that he had always before him the hope that its completion might enable him to devote the rest of his life to sport.[1] Few authors can have had ambition so magnificently fulfilled. *The Manual* covers every form of rural sport, including all the lesser games, and contains a long section on dogs in which a full description is given of every breed.[2] This was followed, in

[1] During my tenure of office as editor-in-chief of *The Field*, I became very interested in my distinguished predecessor, but found that there was practically nothing about him in the office of the paper he edited so ably for so many years beyond one small notebook in which he made notes, apparently for an autobiography and which contains the statement referred to. There is no portrait of Walsh in *The Field* office. Indeed, the only picture of him appears to be a woodcut published in *The Illustrated London News* at the time of his death in 1888. This has been reproduced recently in Hubbard's *Literature of British Dogs*.

[2] Republished in condensed form as *The Dog* in 1878.

1867, by *The Dogs of the British Islands*, a book composed of articles reprinted from *The Field* and edited by 'Stonehenge', who, of course, contributed himself. This book, which enjoyed a great success and went through five editions, is particularly interesting for its illustrations of famous dogs, among them a very fine engraving of that wonderful greyhound, Master McGrath.

The year 1872 is notable for the publication of the first dog book to be illustrated by photographs—Henry Webb's *Dogs: their Points, Whims, Instincts and Peculiarities*. In the same year Edward Laverack published *The Setter*, which must surely rank as one of the finest treatises on an individual breed ever to be written.[1]

The first volume of Vero Shaw's *The Illustrated Book of the Dog* was published in 1879 and the second in 1881. This sumptuous work contains twenty-seven excellent coloured plates of well-known breeds, and one really bad one, that of the Dalmatian, whose marking is so geometrically precise that one can only suppose that the artist had never seen the breed. Shaw's work became recognised as the authority in its time, and was translated into German, in which country it enjoyed an even greater success than in England.

Twelve years later came Rawdon B. Lee's *A History and Description of the Modern Dogs of Great Britain and Ireland*, published in three volumes, and commonly known as *Modern Dogs*. Rawdon Briggs Lee gave up the editorship of the *Kendal Mercury* in 1883 to become the Kennel Editor of *The Field*, a post which he held for twenty-four years. Lee was a very verbose and not over-careful writer, and his book contains a number of errors.[2] But it is important for two reasons. He was the first of the major authorities to consider the show as the most important thing in the dog world, and he was at pains to publish the opinions (though not always careful to check them) of the leading breed experts of the day, opinions which are the more interesting when considered in the light of modern practice. And, secondly, he published a novel classification of dogs. It was this classification (which will be considered in a

[1] A facsimile edition was published in 1945.

[2] It must not be thought that, because I have from time to time in this chapter pointed out errors on the part of earlier writers, I lay any claim to omniscience. It is the prerogative of each generation to point out the mistakes of its predecessors. I am well aware that, sooner or later, somebody will point out my own mistakes; mistakes of which I am at the moment quite unaware, even as my predecessors were unaware of theirs.

later chapter) which was adopted by the Kennel Club and which forms the basis of their classification to-day.

The opening years of the present century saw the publication of three most important books: James Watson's *The Dog Book* (1906), Arthur Croxton Smith's *British Dogs at Work* (1906) and Robert Leighton's *The New Book of the Dog* (1907).

Watson, except by specialists, is unknown to-day. Even in his lifetime he obviously found it difficult to gain recognition from his countrymen, for his book was originally published in parts in the United States; only after it had gained success there was it published in two volumes in this country. It is a work of profound scholarship, which deals with every aspect of the dog—Watson was himself an all-round sportsman of outstanding skill—and is profusely illustrated with reproductions of early prints and paintings, as well as with photographs of the show champions of the day.

Croxton Smith's book is important, not because of any intrinsic merit, but because it is the first published work of a man who was to be the dominant figure in the British dog world for almost half a century. He was one of the first men to encourage the use of dogs for police work and one of the first to encourage their use in helping blind people. He was, in fact, Chairman of the Guide Dogs for the Blind Association for several years and of the Kennel Club for eleven years. Much that we now take for granted in the dog world owed its inception to Croxton Smith's knowledge and enthusiasm.

Robert Leighton's book quickly became recognised as an authoritative work. It has since been reprinted many times, with periodic revisions. Leighton took immense trouble with his work, and errors are few and far between. Leighton was the first British authority to describe some of the better known breeds of the Continent, and was undoubtedly instrumental in introducing some new breeds to Britain. All the important British breeds of the time are dealt with, some of the chapters being contributed by leading show breeders. The book is exceptionally well illustrated with coloured plates and photographs, and in the subscribers' edition of 1907 (four quarto volumes) there is a coloured frontispiece showing the anatomy of the dog in detail.

Prior to the outbreak of the First World War only one other book was published that merits special mention. This is *Toy Dogs and their Ancestors*, by the Hon. Mrs. Neville Lytton (the present Baroness Wentworth), which was published in 1911 and which remains to this day (though now scarce and commanding a high price on the second-hand market) the standard work on the toy breeds. Certainly no historian of the dog can afford to be without it.

This is true, too, of Edward C. Ash's *Dogs: Their History and Development,* which was published, in two stout volumes, for subscribers in 1927. This magnificent work—now, unfortunately, obtainable only at a price which puts it beyond the reach of all but the wealthy—is undoubtedly the most comprehensive work (within the limits set by its title) to be published in any language, excelling even de Bylant's *Les Races de Chiens* (1894 and subsequent editions). Ash undoubtedly owed a good deal to James Watson and something to Robert Leighton.[1] It is strange, therefore, to find that he makes only one mention of Watson—and that a relatively unimportant one in connection with the Boston Terrier—and no mention whatsoever of Robert Leighton. But, although Ash was indebted to earlier historians—all historians of whatever subject are indebted to the labours of their predecessors—much of his work (indeed, by far the major portion of it) is the result of his own original research in the British Museum and elsewhere. Lavishly illustrated, Ash's sumptuous work must be an indispensable reference for all time.

[1] Just as I am heavily indebted to Watson, Leighton, Ash himself and, indeed, to all previous historians of the dog.

V

THE DOG IN SPORT

THERE can, I think, be little doubt that man's first use of the dog—other than for food—was in the chase. The dogs about the camp would, no doubt, give warning of the approach of strangers, for that is in the nature of the animal, but they cannot on that account be considered 'guard-dogs'. The true guard-dog is the product of training, and primitive man had neither the time nor the patience to train dogs. But the hunting-dog would have required little or no training. He followed his natural instincts, and man followed him. From that simple beginning the rest came easily.

Which breed was first used by man in the chase must remain a matter of opinion. Almost certainly it was a dog of the greyhound type, as shown in the ancient art of the Middle East. But these are not the dogs that figure in the earliest of all sporting literature, Xenophon's *Cynegeticus*. We know that Xenophon's hounds were scenting hounds, for we are told by Arrian that the greyhound was unknown in Greece in the days of the great Greek general and historian, but we would know it equally well from Xenophon's own description of his hounds:

> 'In the first place they ought to be big; and in the second place they should have light, flat, well-knit heads. The lower part of the face should be sinewy and the eyes black, bright and prominent: face, large and broad, with a deep space between the eyes: ears long, thin and bare on the outside: neck long, soft and flexible: breast broad and fleshy: shoulder-blade not at much distance from the shoulders:

the fore-legs small, straight, round and firm: the bend in the legs square, sides not altogether deep but coming together in oblique fashion: loins fleshy and in size medium, neither too soft nor too hard, sides neither large nor small: rounded hips, fleshy at the back and not close together in the upper parts but contracted inwardly, the lower flanks themselves loose: tail long, straight, and pointed: thighs hard, lower thighs long, mobile and compact: legs much more highly developed before than behind, and somewhat slender: agile feet.

'If your hounds are as I have described in appearance they will be strong, light, well-proportioned, swift runners, bright-eyed and clean-mouthed. In hunting they ought soon to learn to quit the beaten tracks, slanting their heads towards the ground, smelling at the tracks but drooping their ears downwards, and while they dart quick glances this way and that, and wag their tails, they should go forward in a body towards the lairs making many deviations. When they are actually near the hare, then they should give the sign to the huntsman, by running about much more quickly than before, signifying by their eagerness, and with the head, the eye and their entire change of carriage, by their looking towards or at the hare's hiding-place, and moving their bodies forwards, backwards and sideways, by their obvious joy and delight, that they are near the hare. They should pursue the animal unremittingly and steadily, with a great noise and barking, penetrating everywhere where the hare does, and run quickly and vigorously after him, twisting with him this way and that, barking loudly withal. And let them not leave the track and return to the huntsman. Apart from having such appearance and being fitted for such duties, they should be of the superior kind in spirit, in speed, in scent and in hair. In the first place they will show spirit if they do not leave the hunting when the stifling heat comes on: and good at the scent if they apprehend the hare in bare, dry and sunny localities at the advent of the dog-star: sound of foot if during the same season of the year their feet are not blistered when they run over mountainous grounds. As to the coating of the hair, it should be fine and thick and soft. As to colour, a dog ought not to be red or black or white altogether: a uniform colour is not a sign of breeding but rather of a common animal.'

This is, really, quite a passable description of a modern harrier; the more so as it is fairly evident from the text (though he does not specifically say so) that Xenophon's ideal hound was a tricolour. But Xenophon's hounds—and it is evident from his book that he was not the first man to hunt hounds in this way—were slow. They did not run the hare down. That was not their purpose. Their purpose was to drive the quarry into nets, which had been carefully sited before the hunt began. The success of the huntsman depended upon his knowledge of the countryside, the ways of the hare, and upon his siting of his nets.

Presumably this sort of hunting was taken up by the Roman gentry and spread by them over western Europe, for we may be sure that when hounds of the Greyhound type first came into southern Europe they came as the prized possessions of the higher ranks of the nobility. Be that as it may, there can be no doubt that hunting with scenting-hounds was well established in France at an early date. Because of this, it is generally accepted that the scenting-hound was first brought into Britain by the Norman conquerors.

That is not the case. There were scenting-hounds in Britain in Roman times, and it is as certain as anything can be that they were not brought in by the Romans but were already well established long before Julius Cæsar made his first excursion. Oppian's poem :

> By painted Britons brave in war they're bred,
> Are Beagles called, and to the chase are led;
> Their bodies small and of so mean a shape,
> You'ld think them curs that under tables gape

suggests that the Beagle is indigenous to Britain. Scholars may question the rendering of Oppian's *Agassoei* as 'beagles', but the subsequent lines of the poem leave no doubt that he was alluding to diminutive hounds. However, we need not rest on Oppian. The word 'beagle' comes from the Celtic *beag* (the modern Welsh *bach*) meaning 'small'. It is the 'brach' of medieval writers. Moreover, we know from Canute's forest laws of 1016 that beagles were in common use in Saxon times, for 'small hounds' are specifically excluded from mutilation.

The Norman kings had a passion for hunting the deer, and the hounds they brought with them were of a large and heavy breed known as the Talbot. The Talbot was the descendant of the St. Hubert hound (so called from the monastery of St. Hubert in the Ardennes)—indeed, it probably differed but little from the true St. Hubert—and its modern descendant is the bloodhound. It was slow but determined, and was ideal for hunting deer in a heavily wooded land.

But it was altogether too slow for hunting the hare. And, despite the fashion set by the Norman kings—a fashion, incidentally, which their rigorous laws prevented anybody from following openly—hare hunting remained here, as elsewhere, the supreme sport. Edward, Duke of York, in his *The Master of Game*, gives the hare precedence over the hart. Indeed, he goes further than that. He says: 'It is to be known that the hare is the king of all venery, for all blowing and the fair terms of hunting cometh of the seeking and the finding of the hare. For certain it is the most marvellous beast that is."

Hunting the hare remained the principal sport of the majority of country squires and farmers until well into the eighteenth century. It is probable that during the fifteenth and sixteenth centuries most country squires and some yeoman farmers kept a few couple of hounds with which they hunted whenever they felt inclined. Indeed, it seems likely that there are very few villages in England and Wales that have not at some time had their own pack of hounds. These packs did not specialise. They did not hunt the hare only; they took what came. William Twici, writing early in the fourteenth century, speaks of hunting hare, hart, boar, wolf and fox. It is often said that fox-hunting in this country is not more than some two hundred years old (and as an organised, specialised, sport that is true enough), but Twici, though he regarded the fox as the least of his quarries, took his fox-hunting seriously:

> 'Draw with your hounds about groves and thickets and bushes near villages; a fox will lurk in rude places to prey upon pigs and poultry, but it will be necessary to stop up earths, if you can find them, the night before you intend to hunt; and the best time will be about midnight, for then the fox goeth out to seek his prey'.

And it is evident that Twici used two types of hounds: a small type for hunting the hare, and a larger type for hunting bigger quarry. But neither type was really specialised. If his large hounds put up a hare, well and good, the hare was hunted.

Specialisation did not commence much before the end of the seventeenth century. William Somervile (1675–1742), who lived at Edstone near Stratford-on-Avon, kept two small packs. In 1735, in his poem 'The Chace', the greatest poem in the literature of sport, he wrote:

'A different hound, for every diff'rent chace,
Select with judgement; nor the timorous hare
O'ermatched destroy, but leave that vile offence
To the mean, murd'rous, coursing crew, intent
On blood and spoil. Oh blast their hopes, just Heaven.'

Somervile practised what he preached. He kept twelve couple of hounds, 'rather rough and wire-haired', with which he hunted the fox and an occasional buck (and a few of which he used for hunting otter during the summer), and twelve couple of harriers, which he had bred from the old Cotswold Hound (which was, in fact, a beagle) and the old Southern Hound, and which he kept solely for hare-hunting.

Peter Beckford (1740–1809) lived at Steepleton Iwerne in Dorset, and also hunted both hare and fox. In his *Thoughts on Hunting* (1779), which is the classic prose work in the literature of the sport, he describes his hare-hounds:

'The hounds, I think, most likely to show you sport, are between the large slow-hunting harrier and the little fox beagle: one is too dull, too heavy, and too slow; the other too lively, too light and too fleet. The first, it is true, have most excellent noses, and I make no doubt will kill their game at last, if the day be long enough; but you know the days are short in winter, and it is bad hunting in the dark. The others, on the contrary, fling and dash, and are all alive; but every cold blast affects them; and if your country is deep and wet, it is not impossible but some of them may be drowned. My hounds were a cross of both these kinds, in which it was my endeavour to get as much bone and strength in as small a compass as possible. It was a difficult undertaking. I bred many years, and an infinity of hounds before I could get what I wanted: I, at least, had the pleasure to see them very handsome; small, yet very bony: they ran remarkably well together; ran fast enough; had all the alacrity you could desire; and would hunt the coldest scent.'

Obviously Peter Beckford's harriers were bred on much the same lines as William Somervile's, for both sprang from crosses between the same two types of hare-hounds, the types then in vogue with the squires of the west and south-west. But it must not be thought that these were the only types of hounds in the country at the time. The anonymous author of *An Essay on Hunting* (1733) says:

'The Hounds most in use and proper for Hare-hunting may be confined to few sorts, and each excellent in nature: to wit, the deep-tongued, thick-lipped, broad and long-hung southern hounds.

'The fleet sharp-nosed Dog, ears narrow and pointed, deep chested, with thin shoulders, portending a quarter of the Fox-strain.

'The rough wire-haired hound, thick-quartered, well-hung, not too fleshy shouldered, together with the rough or smooth Beagle.

'Each of these sorts, as I have said before, have their excellencies, etc. It is not possible, with justice, to commend one before another, for kind, colour, or service, preference being given according to the humours and inclinations of Sportsmen, the tribe of whom are very numerous, and, of consequence, different in opinion.

'He that delights in a long chace of six hours, often more, and to be in with the dogs all the time, let him breed of the southern Hounds first mentioned, or such heavy dogs as Sussex Gentlemen run in the weald. They make good deep bass musick, afford great diversion, and, considering how dirty the country is (notwithstanding a hunt often lasts all day long), fatigue the healthy footman very little.

'In an open counry where there is good riding, prefer the second sort, with a quarter of Fox-strain: these suit the more eager, active Horseman, and spend their tongues generously, making delightful harmony, and at the same time go at such a rate a hare durst not play many tricks before them; they seldom allow her time to loiter; she must run and continue her foiling or change soil, if the latter she dies....

'The slow hounds mentioned generally pack best. Of the second sort, many not being of equal speed (for it is hard to procure an even kennel of fast Hounds) will be found to tail, which is an inconveniency....

'The southern Dogs are not so guilty of running a-head; for as they pack well together, from their equality of speed (it being easier to excel the slow than the fast) at the least balk there are ten noses on the ground for one.

'The third species of Hounds mentioned I never saw an entire kennel of, being in some parts not much encouraged; they are of the northern breed, and in great esteem, being bold Dogs, and by many Huntsmen preferred for Otter and Marten: in some places they are encouraged for Foxhounds, but bad to breed from, being too subject to degenerate and produce thick, low, heavy shouldered Dogs unfit for the chace.

'Beagles, rough or smooth, have their admirers; they spend their tongues freely in treble or tenor, and go at a greater rate than the Southern Hounds, but tail abominably. They run low to the ground, therefore enjoy the scent better than taller Dogs, especially when the atmosphere lies low.'

It will be seen that there were then, in the eighteenth century, three distinct types of harriers and two types of beagles. It will have been noticed, too, that the anonymous author of *An Essay on Hunting*, while firmly wedded to hare-hunting, mentions (as do William Somervile and Peter Beckford, both hare-hunters first and foremost) the foxhound as a particular type, and also another quite distinct type, the 'heavy dogs' used by Sussex gentlemen in the weald. To-day there are still three distinct types of harriers, but the beagles, though they vary a little in height from pack to pack according to the country over which they hunt, are now all of one type and, beyond doubt, a vast improvement on anything known in the eighteenth century.

Of the three types of harrier still to be found in Britain the oldest, undoubtedly, is that which hunts the Holcombe country in Lancashire. The Holcombe Harriers are a very old pack—they have been kennelled at Holcombe for more than two hundred years—and they have kept fairly true to the old type of hound; that is, to the old Southern Hound.[1] In *The Sportsman's Cabinet* there occurs this description of the Southern Hound:

'This hound, formerly so very highly estimated, is readily distinguished by his superior size, great strength and majestic solemnity of appearance; in the body he is long, in the carcase round, chest deep, ears long and sweeping, with a tone in the cry, peculiarly deep, mellow and attracting. From the particular formation of the olfactory organs, or from the extra secretion of glandular moisture which always adheres to the nose and lips, or to some other latent cause, it is endued with the most exquisite sense of smelling, and often distinguishes the scent an hour after the lighter beagles have given it up: their slowness affords them opportunity to receive the assistance and instruc-

[1] 'Southern' had no connection with the south of England. It was not known as the Southern Hound in Lancashire because it came from the south of England but because it came from France.

tions of the huntsman, in a much greater degree than those of a fleeter description; but as they are so well enabled to hunt a cold scent they are too apt to make it so, by their tardiness in action, and too minute exactness.'

But the Southern Hound, though best known in Lancashire, occurred elsewhere. Delabere Blaine, in his *Encyclopædia of Rural Sports*, says:

'The old Southern Hound . . . was formerly strong and large, with a monstrous head, overhanging chaps, full in the throat and dew-lapped. This dog is now rarely met with; but a somewhat lengthened type is occasionally seen, and they still preserve the general character. In colour the Southern Hound is mottled, pied or liver coloured, and sometimes nearly black, but in such cases the tintings are elegantly relieved with tan markings. . . . Until within thirty or forty years, the heavy deep-flewed Southern Hound was to be met with in several inclosed and deeply earthed counties. As irrigation drained the lands, and cultivation improved the soil, and enabled the sportsman to follow the chase on horseback, a lighter breed was employed. But even within a very few years, the Weald of Sussex was hunted by these slow hounds, whose bass music raised the echo around, and made the welkin ring. The want of speed in this dog is admirably compensated for by his unerring nose and his determined perseverance, which thus makes the trial between the pursuers and the pursued on an equality, and also enables the followers to become witnesses of every stratagem of the hare, and every hit of the dogs. The general *rush* to the head, which would delight the modern hare hunter, would have distanced the olden one, even had he been mounted on the stately palfrey or the domestic pad.

'The old Sussex blue mottled harriers, which formed perhaps the first step in the fining of the original stock, are now nearly extinct, and only to be met with in the weald of that county, some heavy parts of Kent, and a few other vicinities.'

Blaine is, of course, confusing two distinct types—the Southern Hound and the 'heavy dogs' of the Sussex weald, which were Talbot or St. Hubert hounds, or their direct descendants Bloodhounds. But he does indicate the change in type and the reasons for it, and in doing so he gives us a hint as to the origin of the modern Foxhound. There was, as we have seen, a Foxhound—or at least a hound used for hunting foxes—long before this. Probably the earliest pack used exclusively for hunting foxes was the Charlton in Sussex, which went back to 1689. But these hounds would not have been different in any particular way from the hounds that had been common to the British countryside for generations. They were used for a particular purpose because that was the whim of their owner; they were not different dogs.

There was no sudden development of the Foxhound. I doubt very much if there was any deliberate development at all; at least, in the beginning. It is often said that the modern Foxhound was fashioned by crossing the Southern Hound with the Northern Hound (the old 'Fox Beagle'), a lighter, longer-legged animal adapted for work in hill country. John Scott, in his *The Sportsman's Repository*, says that a greyhound cross was also used. I agree with my friend Henry Higginson that this is so unlikely that it may be dismissed as a flight of the imagination. But, no doubt, the blood of the Southern and the Northern Hound was mixed here and there, and every now and again. But it was not so that the modern Foxhound was made. Indeed, the modern Foxhound was not made. The breed evolved to meet changing conditions. Blaine mentions the three most important of these: the draining of the land, the improvement and spread of cultivation and the employment of horses by hunt followers. It was the last, made possible by the other two, that was the deciding factor in the evolution of the Foxhound. Horses became steadily faster, and it was necessary to have hounds to go with them. All this was achieved, not by out-crossing to greyhounds, but by careful selection within the pack and by clever out-crossing to selected hounds of other packs. Once conditions made it possible, hound breeding became a science. The Foxhound Kennel Stud Book has been published continuously since 1800, and to-day the breeding of Foxhounds is a science every whit as closely studied as that of the breeding of Thoroughbreds, but a science very much more complex, since packs differ from each other in size and conformation according to the type of country over which they work.

The greatest difference of this sort is to be seen, of course, in the Welsh Foxhound. But then this is, in fact, an entirely different animal. A stoutly built animal with a rough, rather shaggy coat, it has a remarkable nose and a most musical voice. There are to-day few purely Welsh packs of Foxhounds; there has been much crossing with English hounds. This has been done, of course, in order to combine the best qualities of both. Some breeders, notably the late Sir Edward Curre, have achieved great success with cross-bred packs. But success has not been uniform by any means, especially in hill country.

Two other types of scenting-hounds must be considered here, the Staghound and the Otterhound. The Staghound proper no longer exists in Britain. The last pack of them, which hunted Exmoor, was sold to Germany in 1825. They were large animals, some twenty-eight to thirty inches high, and were almost certainly very slow. What their stamina was like we do not know, but in view of their size it does not seem likely to have been very great. They had wonderful voices—all their contemporaries remark on this feature—and they are said to have been excellent even on a cold scent. They would certainly have been quite unsuited to present-day conditions. From 1825 onwards, deer have been hunted by drafts from foxhound and harrier packs. Some staghound packs now breed their own hounds, but there are so few packs in the country, and most of the hunting is so artificial in its conception, that no definite staghound type is now likely to arise.

Otter hunting is a very ancient sport. It is first mentioned in English historical records in 1175, when by a charter of Henry II, which is still preserved in the Record Office, Roger Follo was appointed 'King's Otter Hunter'. From that time onwards there are a large number of records showing how keen was the royal interest in the sport. King John was a real enthusiast and took a deep personal interest in the performance of his hounds, and would dispatch them to different parts of the country. In July 1212 he sent his pack to the Sheriff of Somerset, ordering him to provide necessaries for:

> 'Ralph the huntsman and Godfrey his fellow, with two men and two horses and twelve otter hounds as long as they find employment in capturing otters in your shire. And as soon as they cannot capture any you are forthwith to send them back to us, and any cost you may incur through them shall be accounted to you at the Exchequer.'

John le Oterhunte was appointed huntsman to Edward I. Edward II had a pack of twelve Otterhounds and two Greyhounds under the charge of two feeders, and William Twici was his huntsman, though curiously enough he does not mention otter hunting in his book. Edward III issued a decree expressly forbidding the killing of otters except by packs of hounds. Henry IV appointed William Melbourne to be his 'Valet of our Otterhounds', and his son, John Melbourne, was appointed 'Keeper of the King's Dogges for the Otter Hunting' by

Henry VI. (William Melbourne, incidentally, appears to have written on the subject of otter hunting, for the Duke of York, in his *The Master of Game*, writing of the otter, says: 'Of the rest of his nature I refer to Melbourne, the King's otter hunter.' Unfortunately, Melbourne's treatise has been lost.) Indeed, from the time of Henry II to the end of Charles II's reign, we have a complete list of Masters of the Royal Otterhounds. The last to be appointed was Simon Smith in 1684.

It must not be thought that because all our monarchs from Plantagenets to Stuarts kept a pack of otterhounds, all were keen otter hunters. There can be little doubt that, at least until Stuart times, the Royal Otterhounds were maintained primarily to keep in check an animal harmful to fish and not simply for sport. Fish in those days formed a much more important part of the people's diet than it does to-day, and the fisheries of our rivers were a very valuable source of the nation's food supply. The royal otterhounds were kept, not only as part of the duty that the King owed to his people, but also as an example to large landowners to do likewise.

We have no means of knowing what these early otterhounds looked like. For that matter, there has been a great deal of argument about the origin of the modern Otterhound. It has been suggested that it springs from a fusion of Northern and Southern Hound blood, crossed first with some variety of Water Spaniel and then with a large variety of Terrier. Other authorities have suggested that to this mixture there has been added Bloodhound and Welsh Foxhound. But there can be no doubt that the true, shaggy-coated Otterhound—the hound of the Dumfriesshire and the Kendal and District packs—springs from the Griffon-Vendéen, which is still to be found hunting in parts of France. The Griffon-Vendéen is itself derived from a cross between the Griffon de Bresse, the oldest known scent-hunting hound in Europe, and the smooth Vendéen, which is almost as old.

But the true Otterhound is rare in Britain to-day. Almost all the packs are mixed. Draft foxhounds are extensively used, and almost all the packs are now composed largely, if not entirely, of these and foxhounds too old for the hunting field. It takes some time—perhaps even as long as two years—to enter a Foxhound to otter, and the best are those that have never been entered to fox. Draghounds, on the other hand, are good. If a hound will hunt a drag, it is not a difficult matter to make him hunt anything else.

Irish Wolfhound.

Borzoi.

Mastiff.

Pug.

THE DOG IN SPORT

THE GREYHOUND

Hunting with 'running dogs'—that is, those that pursue their quarry by sight rather than by scent—is probably the oldest form of hunting with dogs in the world. We do not know how old, but it seems probable that it was practised in Egypt, both with hares and gazelles, at least as long ago as 2000 B.C.

However, the first detailed account we have of sport with Greyhounds is from Arrian (Flavius Arrianus, A.D. 95–175), the author of the first treatise ever to be written on an individual breed. Arrian calls the Greyhound the 'Gallic' Hound. He was distressed by the prevalent use of nets as advocated by Xenophon, but he is careful to point out that Xenophon did not know the Gallic Hound:

> 'That he knew of no dogs equal to the Gallic dogs in speed appears from this: he says that hares caught by dogs are caught because they are defective in natural speed or by good luck. Now, if he had known the Gallic dogs, he would, I think, have made a similar remark about these dogs and have said the hares escape them only when they are not good specimens of the breed or by good luck. For no hare could escape them if they were the best specimens in body and breed, unless helped by the roughness of the country, or by hiding or some similar cause.'

But now that the Gallic Hound is known, he begs his countrymen to give up the use of nets and to hunt the hare in the manner of the Gauls, telling them that:

> 'The aim of true sportsmen with hounds is not to take the hare, but to engage her in a racing contest or duel, and they are pleased if she happens to escape.'

He then goes on to give a description of a good Greyhound; a description, particularly for the points indicating speed, which holds good for the modern Greyhound. He gives advice on the entering of dog puppies:

> 'Dog puppies must not be taken out coursing until they are two years old, for their limbs become set at a much later period than those of bitches. Besides, it is attended with no little danger to take them out earlier, many a greyhound having been prematurely destroyed by a severe course before he was full grown, and especially those of the greatest spirit and highest breeding, for in consequence of their spirit they run to the very utmost of their power. A bitch is much faster than

> a dog, but a dog is hardier, and preferable because it will run at any time of the year, and also because it is much rarer to find a good dog than a good bitch, and a dog preserves its speed up to its tenth year, but a bitch is valuable if it keeps it till its fifth year.'

The principles governing coursing, as laid down by Arrian, have remained fundamentally unchanged to the present day:

> 'Whoever has good greyhounds should never lay them in too near the Hare, nor run more than two at a time. For though the animal is very swift and will oftentimes beat the dogs, yet, when she is first started, she is so terrified by the hollo-ing, fear, and, in the confusion, very often, the best sporting Hares are killed without showing any diversion. She should therefore be suffered to run some distance from her form, and recollect her spirits, and then, if she is a good sporting Hare, she will lift up her ears, and stretch out with long strides from her seat, the dogs directing their course after her with great activity of limb, as if they were leaping, affording a spectacle worthy the trouble that must necessarily be employed in properly breeding and training these dogs.'

Almost two thousand years of coursing experience has gone to support Arrian's wisdom.

It is usually stated that the first coursing meeting in England was held at Swaffham in Norfolk in 1776. Turbervile, however, makes it clear that meetings were held in 1576, and there is nothing to suggest that these were the first ones. Indeed, it is obvious that Turbervile is describing something that he regarded as fairly commonplace. It is worthy of note, too, that his chapter on coursing is his own work, for the French author whose work he was translating had nothing to say about it. After describing the methods used, Turbervile goes on:

> '. . . And for the better deciding of all these questions, if it be a solemn assembly, they use to appoint judges which are expert in coursing and shall stand on the hillside whither they perceive the hare will bend, to mark which dog doeth best, and to give judgment thereof accordingly.'

This can only refer to organised coursing meetings.

Coursing is now under the control of the National Coursing Club, which was founded in 1858. But it is worthy of note that the laws governing the sport are, with minor variations, those drawn up for Queen Elizabeth I by the Duke of Norfolk. The *Greyhound Stud Book* was founded in 1882.

The one name in the coursing year which is known to everybody is the Waterloo Cup, an event analogous in the public mind to the Derby, the Grand National, the Cup Final and the Boat Race. The Waterloo Cup is the name of a stakes run annually in February by the Altcar Coursing Club. This Club was established in 1825 by Viscount Molyneux, and the meetings were held (as they are to-day) on the property of his father, the Earl of Sefton, at Altcar near Liverpool. The Cup itself was established in 1836, the first race being won by Lord Molyneux with 'Milanie'. The prize that year was a silver snuff-box in addition to the stakes, the entry fee being two pounds. The entry fee is now thirty pounds, and the race, in addition to the Cup, is worth about one thousand pounds to the winner.

The list of winners of the Waterloo Cup includes many almost legendary names. 'Master McGrath' is the one best remembered to-day, perhaps because he was taken to Windsor to be introduced to Queen Victoria. 'Master McGrath' won the Cup three times in four starts, in 1868, 1869 and 1871, and was undoubtedly a very good dog. But his record was eclipsed by 'Fullerton', who won in 1889 (when he divided with Troughend), 1890, 1891 and 1892. 'Cerito', a little bitch of fifty-one pounds, was also a triple winner—in 1850, 1852 and 1853. 'Coomassie', another bitch, and certainly the smallest in all the long list of winners, for she weighed only forty-four pounds, won in 1877 and 1878. Double winners are rare. The last was 'Swinging Light' in 1941 and 1942. Before that one has to go back to 1900 and 1901 for a double winner, 'Fearless Footsteps'.

GREYHOUND RACING

No discussion of the dog in sport would be complete without reference to greyhound racing. This is usually considered to be a new sport in Britain, the year of birth being given as 1926. In fact, the first greyhound race in England was held in 1876 at the Welsh Harp, Hendon. The artificial hare was propelled by a windlass which was operated by hand. The track was straight and the fastest dog won. And it was because of this that the sport died. Form was too consistent for worth-while betting. The promoters realised that the straight track was to blame, and took out a patent for a circular track, but then let the matter drop.

Whippet racing has, of course, been popular in England, particularly in the north, for many years, and may properly be considered as the father of greyhound racing in Britain. Whippet racing is 'straight running'—that is, on a straight track—the lure being a handkerchief, which the dog's owner, standing at the far end, waves frantically. The dogs are separated the one from the other by strings. Provided that the handicapping is skilfully done, whippet racing is a most attractive and exciting sport, and there is, contrary to general opinion, very little trickery connected with it. The races are short—the standard distance is 200 yards—and are over in a flash. A good dog will cover 200 yards in about twelve seconds.

Perhaps, if the Welsh Harp promoters had gone in for skilful handicapping, we should have had organised greyhound racing all over the country fifty years or more ago. As it was, the sport first gained favour in the United States.

Shortly after the end of the First World War an Oklahoma farmer, O. P. Smith, was summoned for coursing a hare in an enclosed paddock. (This, by the way, is also illegal in England.) Unwilling to give up his sport, he searched the records and found the old patent, which he acquired. He then proceeded to build a circular track at Oklahoma City. Within a year or two, the sport had spread all over the United States, and O. P. Smith was a very rich man.

In 1924 Mr. Charles Munn, an American, brought the sport to England, and, in partnership with Brigadier Critchley, formed a track-owning company (now the Greyhound Racing Association) and established the first race-track at Belle Vue, Manchester. The new sport got off to a slow start, but once it had captured the public imagination, it spread as rapidly through England as it had previously done through the United States. The first London track was at Harringay.

Other track-owning companies soon sprang up, and it became obvious that a controlling body was needed. The National Coursing Club was approached, but refused to co-operate, pointing out that its function was to safeguard the interests of coursing. So the National Greyhound Racing Club was formed in 1928. This body drew up the rules of racing, registered all tracks of repute and the dogs racing on them, and to-day stands in much the same relation to the sport as does the Jockey Club to flat racing.

In the beginning there was great opposition on the part of the coursing world to greyhound racing. It was widely held that, as all sorts of inexperienced people would be tempted to breed and sell, there would be a flood of third-rate animals; and that, even if this did not happen, there would inevitably be a compulsion to breed for speed only, to the detriment of the breed as a whole. Nothing of the sort has happened. Speed alone is not enough to ensure success on the race-track. A dog must have brains as well. Races are frequently lost and won on the bends; it is a clever dog which can use a bend to its advantage. Quite apart from this, the big prizes and the intense competition has meant that the inferior dog stands no chance at all. I think that there can be no doubt that, so far from proving detrimental, greyhound racing has actually improved the breed. It would not, however, have done so had there not from the start been wise and firm guidance from the top.

There is some slight difference—apparent, perhaps, only to the expert eye—between the coursing greyhound and the racing greyhound, between a Waterloo Cup winner and a Greyhound Derby winner, which springs from the different nature of their tasks. But there is now an increasing number of dual-purpose dogs, and breeding is becoming more and more closely interwoven.[1] 'Endless Gossip', the winner of the Greyhound Derby, reached the last eight in the Waterloo Cup. 'Burletta', who was the winner of the first Greyhound St. Leger, was the dam of the Waterloo Cup winners of 1933 and 1937, 'Genial Nobleman' and 'Rotten Row'. 'Maesydd Michael', the winner of the Waterloo Cup of 1946, was the son of 'April Burglar', who won many big races on the track. Racing blood is likely to play a larger and larger part in the sterner test of coursing as the years pass.

BAITING SPORTS

Certainly as old as any other form of diversion with dogs are the baiting sports. They were very popular with the Roman crowds and formed an essential feature of all gladiatorial shows, and they were extremely popular throughout Britain at least from Roman times until quite recently.

All the baiting sports were exceptionally cruel. Nowadays we pride ourselves on being a nation of animal lovers—and especially dog-lovers—and we like to think that we have always been so. In fact, this side of

[1] Originally, of course, all track greyhounds came from coursing kennels. Every winner of the Waterloo Cup for the last thirty years traces back to 'Fiery Furnace', and this is, I think, true also of the vast majority of 'Classic' winners on the track.

our character has not, nationally, been manifest for more than a hundred years. Indeed, the multiplicity of animal-protection societies of one sort and another suggests that it is not, even now, correct to say that love of animals is a national characteristic of the British, since there would not, surely, be so many of these societies were there not a need for them.

The baiting sports best known are bull-baiting and bear-baiting. But, in fact, almost every animal that one can think of has been baited in Britain at some time or another, including the horse and the ass. There is a fourteenth-century manuscript which describes the baiting of horses, but this particular diversion seems to have been comparatively short-lived, not because of any pronounced fondness for the horse, but simply because the horse was unable to inflict sufficient damage on the dogs to please the crowds. The baiting of monkeys was very popular, and a fight between a baboon and a dog could always be relied upon to draw a large crowd. There is an Alken print of Jacko, 'the sporting monkey', a baboon that killed a good many dogs in single combat in the heyday of Corinthian England. Very large sums of money were won and lost on Jacko.

Fights between lions and dogs were also very popular with the crowds. In the twenties of the nineteenth century a Mr. Wombwell toured England with two lions, Nero and Wallace, drawing large crowds wherever he went and laying the foundations of a large family fortune. Mr. Wombwell was an astute business-man. Nero always fought first and Wallace a day or two later. At Warwick on 26th July 1825 Nero was pitted against six dogs, which were set on in two batches of three. A dog that turned tailed was deemed to be beaten, and there was to be an interval of twenty minutes between the slipping of each team of dogs. The first team consisted of two large half-bred Mastiffs, weighing about sixty pounds apiece, and a pure-bred Bulldog weighing some thirty pounds. The two large dogs were soon beaten, but the Bulldog stayed eleven minutes and forced the lion to turn tail before being taken out of the cage. The second team, all Bulldogs, pinned the lion by the nose and held him until Mr. Wombwell admitted defeat. Three days later this second team, and another team of pure-bred Bulldogs, were pitted against Wallace. All six dogs were killed, the first contest lasting only five minutes and the second only eight minutes. Mr. Wombwell, who knew his lions very well, was in each case betting on a certainty.

But it was bull-baiting and bear-baiting that captured and held the imagination of the crowds through the centuries. Bull-baiting did not, curiously enough, begin as a sport at all. It was once illegal to slaughter a bull that had not previously been baited with dogs; the idea being that the meat from such a bull was more tender. But the crowds soon decided that the baiting of bulls was rare sport, and flocked in their thousands to watch it. The dogs first used were the old English 'Bandogges', large Mastiffs, the direct descendants of the old dogs of war that gained such fame in the gladiatorial arenas. Mastiffs or mastiff crosses were used until well into the eighteenth century, but by that time bull-baiting had become so much an entertainment in its own right, and quite apart from the butchery trade, that a specialised type of dog was bred for the purpose. The aim in bull-baiting was for the dog to grip the bull by a tender part of the face—preferably the nose or the tongue—and so to hold him still or even to throw him. It was necessary, therefore, for the dog to have tremendous power of jaw, and it was also necessary that the nostrils should be set far enough back to enable the dog to breathe normally without letting go. Thus we developed the Bulldog. But it must not be thought that the Bulldog of the bull-ring bore any resemblance to the squat and wheezing barrel that bears the name to-day. The Bulldog of the bull-ring—certainly the dog of the early nineteenth century when bull-baiting in this country was at its peak and bulls were also specially bred for the sport—had to be lithe and active, as well as powerful, for the bull also knew all the rules of the game.

Bear-baiting never produced a particular type of dog specially bred for the purpose. Bear-baiting, which had almost as long a life in England as bull-baiting, was mere savagery. Although bull-baiting was foully cruel, it was at least a contest between *two* animals, the bull was allowed a certain, though restricted, liberty of movement, and the whole was governed by rules. Nothing of this sort applied to bear-baiting. The bear had no liberty of movement, and as many as eight dogs would be set on to him at one time. All that the crowds wanted to see was blood, and the more blood, the more disembowelled dogs, the better. Both sports were declared illegal in 1835—at the height of their popularity—not so much because they were cruel as because they encouraged undesirable elements in the population to gather together.

The other two very popular baiting sports, dog-fighting and the rat-pit, did produce dogs specially bred for the purpose. The rat-pit was essentially a match between two dogs; a match to see which dog could kill the greatest number of rats within a specified time, or a match to see which could kill a specified number of rats in the shortest time. There was always heavy wagering on the rat-pit, and this, of course, brought about an increasing degree of specialisation. What was required was a dog of considerable intelligence, great stamina, great agility and great strength of jaw. Intelligence was essential. An unintelligent dog, when dropped into the pit, would chase the rats round and round, and kill only a few before he was tired out; the intelligent dog would get the rats on the move and then, scarcely moving himself, would nip them as they passed by him. The expert dogs did not pick up and shake their rats, but merely gave each one a hard bite, breaking the back, and at once passed on to the next. It soon became apparent that long-legged dogs were at a disadvantage; but there was always a controversy about weight. The greatest of all the rat-pit dogs, Billy, a Wire-haired White Terrier with a patched head, weighed twenty-seven pounds, but despite Billy's achievements this was generally considered too heavy (it being agreed that Billy was altogether an exceptional dog), and two short-legged types were evolved: the Yorkshire Terrier, weighing between seven and ten pounds, and the Manchester Terrier (the old Black-and-tan Terrier), weighing about fifteen pounds. Looking at the modern Yorkshire Terrier, it is difficult to believe that this breed once had a national reputation as a ratter.

It is to dog-fighting that we owe the Staffordshire Bull Terrier. Dog-fighting in Britain goes back, of course, to Roman times, but it became really popular only with the abolition of bull- and bear-baiting. The dogs used were Bull Terriers, but by 1860 these had become to separate into two types; the one known as the English Bull Terrier and the other as the Staffordshire Bull Terrier, Staffordshire being the centre of the dog-fighting fancy. The former became more and more a show dog, his looks 'improved' from generation to generation. The latter, the old and original breed (though the name is quite new, for the breed for show purposes was not recognised by the Kennel Club until 1935), continued to be bred for the pit. A very remarkable dog was produced, weighing about thirty-five pounds, lean and hard with prodigious neck and back muscles, and of unsurpassed courage. The true fighting Stafford fights to kill, without preliminaries and quite silently. A puppy of a real fighting strain will sometimes fight to kill at three months old. Yet, even those dogs especially bred for fighting—though illegal, the sport still continues spasmodically up and down the country[1]—are wonderfully sweet-tempered with children, and extraordinarily good with cats.

SHOOTING

Shooting, the most recent of our fields sports, has had a tremendous influence upon the sporting dog, leading to the development of a number of specialised breeds. Dogs were used in connection with game long before the discovery of gunpowder, of course. For example, dogs of some sort were necessarily used in the sport of falconry for the purpose of finding and flushing the game at which the sportsman flew his goshawks or falcons. But it was only with the development of the gun that the gundog became specialised, and increasingly so with each new development in technique in the shooting field.

Originally, all that was required was a dog that would perform for the gun part of the function which it performed for the falconer. What was wanted was a dog which would find game but would not flush it until the shooter was within range. And the range of the early fowling-pieces was very limited. The first dogs used in the shooting field were Setting Spaniels, to be followed very shortly by Pointers. There is really no difference in the essential function performed by setters and pointers.

Retrieving came later, though not, perhaps, much later. Here, the first requirement must, surely, have been retrieving from water. Just as setter and pointer were first developed in Spain, so we must look to the Iberian Peninsula for the development of the Retriever. This was, undoubtedly, the animal that is known to-day as the Cao d' Agua, the Portuguese Water-dog, the ancestor of the Irish Water Spaniel and the Poodle. As the range of the gun increased, so the Setting Spaniel began to give place to the Cocking or Springing Spaniel; and as the drive began to take the place of walking-up, so the Pointer began to give place to the Retriever proper. From that point onwards development proceeded very largely according to personal whim. The multiplicity of breeds of Retriever and Spaniel, each differing a little in appearance but each performing very much the same functions, has not been due, as is so often said, to local requirements but to the whims of owners. Recently, in the shooting field, there has, however, been a new development which is really no more than a putting back of the clock. Economic conditions, a period of great prosperity (at least for a few), made possible the shoot

[1] J. Wentworth Day: *The Dog in Sport*, pp. 185–188.

on the grand scale with an army of beaters driving carefully reared birds in their hundreds to a line of waiting guns, which itself created the demand for the Retriever pure and simple. Economic conditions have killed that type of shoot and brought about a demand for the old dual-purpose dog, the Springer Spaniel, in place of the specialist Retriever.

FIELD TRIALS

Specialisation in the shooting field has given rise to a new competitive sport—the Field Trial. Field Trials, which are comparatively new, were not orginally designed as a competitive sport. They were designed to test the working qualities of gundogs which were regularly worked in the shooting field by their owners. They have grown to be a sport in their own right only since the end of the First World War, perhaps only since the late twenties of this century.

The first trial at which birds were shot to the dogs was held on 10th and 11th September 1867, on the estate of Richard Lloyd Price at Bala in North Wales. Lloyd Price owned some 64,000 acres, and his chief interests in life were shooting and the study of gundogs. It may be said that Field Trials could not have got off to a better start. These first trials were for Pointers, Setters and Retrievers. The first trial for Spaniels did not come until 1899. But Field Trials on a highly organised and competitive scale are purely a thing of this century.

There are, of course, some differences between Retriever trials and Spaniel trials, differences inherent in the nature and purpose of the dogs. There are also differences as between trial and trial, differences dictated by the nature of the ground, weather conditions and so on. But, broadly speaking, the routine at all trials is the same. The draw for the order of the dogs on the card is made by ballot, the judges take up position in the line—there are three judges at Retriever trials; two judges and a referee at Spaniel trials; each judge has two guns to shoot for him —and the dogs are taken in the order of the draw. The card is gone through until every dog has been tried once. After that the judges may call up dogs for trial in any order they wish.

A Retriever trial is exactly what the name implies. A Spaniel has to do more than merely retrieve. The retrieving must be good, of course, but a Spaniel must also find the game to be shot, and the manner in which he does this is very important. There is, therefore, this great difference between Retriever trials and Spaniel trials : the Retriever has to wait for work, the Spaniel is working all the time.

It would be true to say that in all Field Trials the dogs are tested for their ability to find game (that is, to retrieve game), their intelligence and their obedience, with the addition, in the case of spaniels, their ability to put up game for the guns. It all sounds simple enough. It is, in fact, very far from simple. This sort of test cannot be governed by rule. Each dog works in a different way, each has a style of its own. Style is an indefinable quality. Pace, drive, nose—all these things are quite individual and indefinable. Furthermore, they are all, to some extent, governed by the conditions ruling at the time that the dog is tested. For example, the wind may change (and even a very slight change, though a man might not notice it at all, will be of vast importance to the dog) between the trial of one dog and the next in the draw. The humidity may change, and again a very slight change will affect conditions for the dog, though it will not be noticed by a man. These are factors which it is quite impossible to confine within the sort of rules that normally govern competition. And there are other things, which at first sight would appear easy to judge and which in practice are by no means easy. It is, for example, considered very bad for a Spaniel or Retriever to have a 'hard' mouth. It may be thought that it is easy enough to judge a hard mouth; in fact, it is not always a simple matter to judge what caused the damage. In addition to all these things, there is the undoubted fact that judges have very different ideas about such things as style—and, incidentally, about dogs.

Again the tests set by the judges, quite apart from the variations caused by changing conditions which must and do occur in the course of every trial, are never the same from trial to trial. In the very nature of things they cannot be. The tests have, obviously, to depend on the nature of the ground over which the trial is held. Walking-up game and shooting it as it rises is the fairest way of testing Retrievers. But walking-up roots is a very different matter from walking-up bracken; walking-up ground with a good cover a very different matter from walking-up ground with little or no cover. When cover is really scarce, then game must be driven. But driving provides an entirely different test. A dog may be excellent at walking-up and hopelessly wild at driven game.

And there is yet one more factor for which the rules do not allow and cannot allow, and that is the quality and performance of the guns. To have a trial fair beyond all question, one would require six guns, all equally good and all equally in form on the particular day. That just does not happen.

Taking all these things into consideration, one may well ask if a Field Trial does really reveal the quality of a dog. One may well ask if Field Trials really serve any useful purpose at all.

Well, it is very difficult indeed for a dog to become a Field Trial champion. The title of champion is granted to any pointer or retriever which wins two first prizes at two different Field Trials in Open or All-aged Stakes. There are rather more conditions attached to the granting of the title to a spaniel, but, roughly speaking, it is granted to any spaniel which wins three first prizes at three different Field Trials in Open or All-aged Stakes, provided that there are not fewer than eight runners in each stake. In addition to this, a Championship Stake is held each year for Pointers and Setters, for Retrievers, for Spaniels (other than Cockers) and for Cockers. The quality of these champions varies from year to year (as does the quality of the Derby winner), but, as with the Derby, it is usually the best dog on the day that wins. As a number of champions always compete in these Championship Stakes, the winner has some right to be considered the Supreme Champion of the year, though that title is not, in fact, used. It will be appreciated that a dog really has got to be pretty good to win two first prizes, let alone three, in Open or All-aged Stakes. At least, he has got to be pretty good at Field Trials. Whether he will be equally good in the ordinary shooting field is another matter.

The fact is that a Field Trial is quite unlike an ordinary day's shooting. There can be no doubt that the Field Trial provides an excellent test for the dog. But it is quite likely to spoil him for an ordinary day's shooting. The purpose of a Field Trial is to test the dog; the purpose of a day's shooting is to kill game. The two things are not necessarily the same at all. For one thing, the competitive spirit is absent from the day's shooting. This competitive spirit has meant that considerable importance is attached to speed, and speed is really unimportant in the shooting field. I do not know how many Field Trial champions are habitually used by their owners in the shooting field. I suspect very few indeed. They would be much too fast. There is now, in fact, a distinction to be drawn between the Field Trial dog and the gundog. The sport has produced its own type. There is, as yet, no real difference in appearance. But I do not think that there can be any doubt that there soon will be. Indeed, it is inevitable. We are witnessing the evolution of a new animal.

This is an excellent thing. No one would deny that thoroughbred racing is a highly specialised sport and that the Thoroughbred is a highly specialised animal. Equally, no one would dream of denying that the Thoroughbred has had an enormous influence for good on horse-breeding throughout the country—on hunters and many other animals that will never see a racecourse in their lives. In just the same way, the Field Trial is a highly specialised sport, and the Field Trial dog (whether Pointer, Setter, Retriever or Spaniel) on the way to becoming a highly specialised animal. Already, there has been a marked improvement in the standard of the ordinary gundog, for Field Trial champions are in demand for breeding.

VI

THE DOG IN THE SERVICE OF MAN

IF man first made use of the dog in the chase, in the capture of food—and I do not think that there can be any doubt about that—it was not long before he was making use of the animal's natural instincts in other directions. And the first of these was, surely, as a guard. Here, as with the chase, there would, at the start, be no need for training. The dog is by nature possessive, and has a very highly developed sense of territory—these characteristics can be observed in the Pariah and other wild dogs of to-day—and this sense of ownership has given him an acute awareness of approaching danger. Once the initial barrier had been surmounted, once contact had been established between man and dog, and the latter had been brought into or around the camp—and this would have been achieved easily enough by the simple process of putting out food, the bones from a meal and so forth, and would have been a natural step for man to take, since he would have been very anxious to keep contact with the animals who assisted him so greatly in the capture of food—the rest followed naturally. In a matter of a few days (consider how quickly a tamed Pariah adopts his new home and develops a guard attitude towards it and its owners) the dogs would accept the camp as part of their territory, and the humans about the camp with it. The fact that the camp would always be moving, as it would have been with nomad peoples, would tend to focus the territory sense on the camp itself, as the source of food and warmth, and so increase the sense of ownership. It was a reciprocal arrangement; warning in return for food and warmth.

With the early civilisations we find the guard-dog already far advanced, an animal bred specially for the purpose. The Assyrians, the Babylonians, the Chinese, the Egyptians, the Greeks, the Romans, all made great use of the guard-dog. All used large and powerful animals of the mastiff type, each perfectly capable of killing a man. It is evident from the thick collars and chains portrayed in early sculptures and drawing that these massive dogs were normally kept chained up, though they would be released at night to wander about the courtyards of their owners' houses. Nomad man required warning only of the approach of other nomads and of dangerous wild beasts, and this the hunting-dogs would give him as they lay around the camp-fire. But once urban civilisations were established, bringing with them, as all such civilisations do, a large under-privileged class with a big criminal element, something more than mere warning was required. Now actual protection was necessary; hence the emphasis on size and ferocity.

The guard-dog pure and simple had its hey-day in ancient Egypt and Imperial Rome, and though to much less extent, in Norman and Plantagenet England. In Imperial Rome, at any rate, there was a large criminal population which seems to have been fairly well organised, and there was certainly a very inadequate police force. In the England of the Normans and the early Plantagenets, there was a fairly large vagrant population of desperate men. The combination of improved state control, the greater authority of the central government, improved communications, and improved weapons meant that less reliance had to be placed on the guard-dog. To-day we have more or less returned to the situation familiar to the early nomads. What we require of a guard-dog now—if we require a guard-dog at all—is warning. We no longer require an animal to give us physical protection, only one that will give us time to get to the telephone. Thus there is to-day—except in certain military establishments—no need for a specialised guard-dog. Certainly there is no need for size. Indeed, in our modern world with its emphasis on the small house and the flat, size in a dog is more often than not a distinct drawback. The sharp and nippy Terrier with a loud bark makes as good a guard-dog as any, and requires no training.

Nowadays one hears a great deal about the training of guard-dogs, and, indeed, a great deal about the training of dogs altogether; obedience tests and the like. So far as the guard-dog is concerned, I do not believe that there has ever been any really specialised training—except, perhaps, in actual killing, and even then the training consisted only of teaching the dog that his handler was sacrosanct—nor the need for it. All that has to be done is to encourage the dog's natural instinct.

An obedience test with well-trained dogs is a most impressive sight. And, let there be no doubt about it, obedience training is a very highly skilled business. But, let there also be no doubt about it, the skill required to train even the most perfect 'obedience' dog is as nothing compared to the skill required to train a good sheepdog. And how little is this realised!

SHEEPDOGS AND HERDING DOGS

It is not known when or where man first trained dogs to herd and guard his flocks. It was certainly first achieved a very long time ago, for we know that there were shepherd-dogs thousands of years before Christ.

This was, and remains, man's greatest achievement in relation to the dog. In training a dog to hunt or to guard his property, all that man had to do was to encourage the dog's natural instincts. But to train a dog to herd and care for sheep or cattle meant achieving a complete reversal of the dog's natural instincts, for the dog is a carnivorous animal and a hunter, and these are his natural prey. We should always remember when we see the disciplined dogs at an obedience test, when we see a guide-dog leading a blind man, when we see a police-dog at work, that the greatest dog trainer of all time was that illiterate, skin-clad nomad who, many thousands of years ago, probably on the steppes of central Asia, first succeeded in reversing the natural instincts of the dog.

To-day, there are sheepdogs or herding dogs in, I believe, every country in the world, and their number must be legion.[1] Every one of them has to be trained, and this is done, as a rule, by men who do not consider that they have done anything very wonderful and the vast majority of whom would not claim to be dog trainers at all, considering it to be no more than part of the much more important work of shepherding. Yet, in the matter of training, there is no dog in the world comparable to the trained sheepdog.

The stories about the intelligence and cleverness of sheepdogs are legion. One, a classic, was told by James Hogg, the Ettrick Shepherd.

[1] It has been estimated that there are some 320,000 sheepdogs working daily in Australia alone.

St. Bernard.

Newfoundland

Bulldog (old type).

Bulldog.

Hogg was given a sheepdog, named Sirrah, then aged twelve months, because he had 'a somewhat surly and unsocial temper' and made a thoroughly unsatisfactory pet. The dog, when he came to Hogg, had never turned a sheep in his life. But, once in Hogg's hands, his eagerness to learn was so great that within a few months his new owner was able to describe him as 'beyond comparison the best dog I ever saw'. One night a large flock scattered in three different directions over the hills. Hogg called his dog. 'Sirrah,' he said, 'they're a' awa'.' It was a pitch-dark night, but Sirrah immediately set off up the hill. By daylight, unassisted by anyone, he had collected all the sheep. Not one was missing.

This story could be capped by hundreds of others. Indeed, everyone who has ever had anything to do with a working sheepdog will have a story about that animal's intelligence and initiative. And they will all be true. Anybody who has watched sheepdog trials or, better still, has had the opportunity of watching Border Collies at work on the hillside will be prepared to believe them capable of anything, will at least know that it is very unwise to disbelieve.

I have myself known a Border Collie bitch come and fetch her shepherd, make it evident to him that there was something seriously amiss, and then lead him more than a mile to a cast ewe. The point, both of this story and that of Sirrah, is that in each case the dog was working on its own, entirely unassisted. Scientists, I understand, deny the faculty of reasoning to the dog. They can never have watched a working sheep-dog.

It is often said that the exceptional intelligence of the working sheep-dog is due to thousands of years of careful breeding, and that a great deal of the work that the dog does is done instinctively and owes nothing to the trainer. There is a grain of truth in this. It is true that the sheep-dog has been carefully bred over a great many years, and the herding instinct is, undoubtedly, deep-rooted in the family. I have myself seen a couple of untrained, town-bred, Cardigan Corgis, on their first visit to the country, round up a flock of ducks and drive them into a corner. It was a most impressive sight and delighted their owner. But had those dogs not been driven off by a couple of farm-hands there might well have been a disaster.

The hunting instinct and the herding instinct are very closely allied. The sheepdog is fundamentally a hunting-dog. One has only to consider the enormous number of sheep killed annually by dogs in this country to realise how strong is the hunting instinct even in the pet dog.[1] Untrained, the sheepdog in contact with sheep would become a killer. It is only by skilful training that man controls the hunting instinct and turns it to his advantage.

The training of a sheepdog is a much more highly skilled business than the training of any other type of dog. Most training is designed to produce unquestioning obedience, the obedience of a slave. The peak of this type of training may be seen at any good Obedience Test. It would be a very simple matter to train any sheepdog [2] (other than some of the modern show-bench specimens) to the highest standards demanded by Obedience Tests—indeed, one member of the family, the Alsatian, has by far the best record of any breed in these tests—but 'slave' obedience would not be of the slightest use in a working sheepdog. Here, the relationship between man and dog has to be on a much higher plane. It is not a matter of master and slave, but a partnership; the dog understanding what he is doing and working with the man; understanding so well what he is doing that he is able to work on his own, out of sight and out of hearing of the man, using his own initiative to meet constantly changing conditions. It will be understood that there can be no stereotyped method of training. Two men from the same part of the country, working under very similar conditions, will employ quite different methods. Individual shepherds and individual sheepdogs (it should always be remembered that the sheepdog is very definitely an individual) have their individual ways. But the aim is always the same, and so is the result—a well-trained, highly intelligent partner. This can be seen at any sheepdog trial.

Sheepdog trials originated in Wales. The first, organised by J. Lloyd Price of Rhiwlas, Bala, was held at Bala on 9th October 1873. It attracted a gathering of some three hundred people from all over North Wales, who watched ten dogs compete. This trial was won by William Thompson, a Scots shepherd who was working in Wales with a Scots bred dog. In the following year, trials were held at Garth in Glamorgan and at Llangollen, and these were followed by trials at Bala, in which the winners from Garth and Llangollen competed. This was the first

[1] The annual average of sheep killed by dogs in Great Britain since 1949 is 5,520. In addition, more than 4,500 sheep are injured by dogs each year, and more than half of these have to be destroyed subsequently.

[2] The Obedience Championship at Crufts, 1956, was won by a Border Collie, Mr. W. H. Shackleton's 'Dash'.

year in which a cup was offered for competition. In 1875 thirty dogs were entered for the Bala trials, and the attendance was over 2,000, a remarkable figure when one remembers how very difficult travel in North Wales was in those days. The Bala trials were bigger still in 1876 and 1877, but in 1878 they were merged in the Llangollen event, which had also been growing rapidly and which were held on a much more convenient site. More than 6,000 people watched the Llangollen trials in that year, and the entries included dogs from England and Scotland. In 1889 the Llangollen trials were attended by Queen Victoria and other members of the Royal Family, a patronage which was a tremendous encouragement to trials throughout Wales. With the exception of the breaks occasioned by the two world wars, sheep-dog trials have been held annually at Llangollen since 1874, and it is by far the oldest meeting of its kind in the world.

It is appropriate that sheepdog trials should have originated in Wales. The use of sheepdogs is as old as the use of sheep, and shepherd-lore is almost as ancient. Sheep were kept all over Great Britain, of course, and therefore sheepdogs and shepherds to work them, but one of the most interesting survivals of shepherd-lore is the use of Welsh numerals in counting sheep, a method which has persisted (for it is still not altogether dead) in certain districts almost from time immemorial. Four collections of these numerals survive. The passage of the years has naturally brought about some variation as between list and list, but no one can doubt the common parentage.

1.	Yan	Een	Yaen	Yan
2.	Tan	Teen	Tyaen	Tyan
3.	Tether	Tethera	Taedere	Tethera
4.	Pathas	Fethera	Meadere	Methera
5.	Pimp	Fip	Mimp	Pimp
6.	Setha	Obera	Haites	Sethera
7.	Letha	Dobera	Saites	Lethera
8.	Hova	Eendie	Hoaves	Novera
9.	Dova	Teendie	Doaves	Dovers
10.	Dik	Tetheradie	Dik	Dick
11.	Yan-a-Dik	Eenabump	Yaen-a-Dik	Yan-a-Dik
12.	Tan-a-Dik	Teenabump	Tyaen-a-Dik	Tyan-a-Dik

The first two lists come from Yorkshire, and were collected by John Crowther and Halliwell Sutcliffe respectively; the remaining two come from Lakeland, and were collected by Alexander Ellis in 1874 and W. T. Palmer fairly recently.

Miss Dorothy Morton, writing in the *Dalesman*, has said:

> 'Comparing the numerals with those of Welsh shepherds, one finds a striking likeness. It is commonly believed that Welsh drovers bringing cattle and sheep into our rural markets introduced the language which was carried into the far remoteness of England's dales and vales. For a long period after this country was Anglicised, Cumberland and Westmorland and other mountainous parts of the north of England were still occupied by Welsh-speaking people, and it is notable that these numerals were almost wholly limited to this area. It is easy, therefore, to imagine that Welsh-speaking British serfs, shepherding the flocks of their Saxon or Scandinavian or Norman overlords, carried on their method of counting in their mother tongue, thus handing down in a rather debased form this strange language.'

Miss Morton has, I think, the rights of the matter. Though it is true that the Welsh drovers have left their mark in many different parts of England—especially in the names of roads and in inn signs—they came too late to affect language. In any case, they spoke English and were selected for the work because they were able to do so. No, the language of the shepherds owes nothing to the Welsh drovers. It goes back to the time when Welsh was the common language of the people of Britain. Moreover, the small variations in the consonants are just what one would expect to find, after the passage of two thousand years, in a speech that was never written down.

The first English sheepdog trial was held at Bryness in 1876, the winner being Walter Telfer of Morpeth in Northumberland, a member of a family which has played a very important part in the evolution of the Border Collie. The first Scottish trial was held at Carnath in the same year, the winner being James Gardner. To-day sheepdog trials are held in every pastoral country in the world. Some, particularly those of east central Europe, take a specialist form to meet the rather specialised conditions under which the dogs work; but most—including those held in Australia, New Zealand, Tasmania, Argentina, the United States, Canada, Eire, South Africa, Kenya and the Falkland Islands—are held under the rules of the International Sheepdog Society, whose headquarters are at Southport in Lancashire.

The International Sheepdog Society was founded in 1906 at Haddington in Scotland by a small band of Scottish enhusiasts. The objects of the new society were defined at the outset as: 'To stimulate interest in the shepherd and his calling; to secure better management of stock by improving the shepherd's dog; to give financial assistance to members (and their widows) in case of need. These objects shall be promoted by the holding of trials, the institution of a Stud Book for sheepdogs, and in any other way calculated to attain them.' Although 'international' in name, the Society was in fact almost entirely Scottish, only two members coming from over the border in Northumberland and none at all from Wales, the home of the sheepdog trial. Though more than one hundred different trials were held annually in Wales at that time, it was to be sixteen years before any Welshman competed in the Society's trials.

Between 1906 and 1914 nine International competitions were held, England winning five and Scotland four. Only two of these matches were held in England. In 1915 the Society was in a very bad way indeed. There was just £5 in the bank, that and no more—no cups, no trophies of any sort, nothing. It was at this juncture, with no possibility of competitions, that an Airdrie solicitor, James A. Reid, was persuaded to take over the secretaryship. Mr. Reid, who combined a genius for organisation with the zeal of a crusader, somehow managed to keep the Society alive through the war years, and he started International Competition again at the very first possible moment, in 1919. In 1922, by invitation, the Welsh came in, and what had been merely an International competition became the International Championship. This meant, naturally, that competition became much keener; and even more keen in the local competitions, for, in order to qualify for entering his country's national trial a shepherd had to win a prize at a recognised local trial. And it was not at all easy to get a local trial recognised by the governing body concerned. This sharp increase in competition naturally brought about a rise in standard, both in dog and shepherd. It also meant that a standard course, based on the course used for the National Championships, came to be adopted throughout the country.

The International Sheepdog Society now organises four trials each year, and is able to give very good prizes at each. These four trials are the three Nationals (England, Scotland and Wales), each of which lasts for two days, and the International, which is the 'supreme championship' and which lasts for three days. The International is held in each country in strict rotation.

Probably round about two hundred dogs are entered for these championship trials each year (the number varies from year to year, of course), and it is difficult enough to enter, let alone to win. Only dogs registered in the Society's Stud Book, and which have won prizes at local competitions, can compete at the National Trials. Only the twelve dogs which do best in these National Trials can be selected for each national team, which means that only thirty-six dogs can compete in the International Championship. There is, therefore, a very severe eliminating process to be overcome before a dog can get to the International Championship. And, once there, the eliminating process becomes yet more severe. There are now preliminary tests. Only the twelve best dogs from these preliminary tests can compete in the 'Supreme Championship' on the third day. That is to say, only twelve from the two hundred or more that started out, only twelve from the thirty-six brilliant dogs which were selected for the International. And when these twelve come to the final day and the Supreme Championship, they face a test which —for distance, number of sheep and time allowed—is the most severe applied to a sheepdog anywhere in the world.

A consideration of the tests applied in the Nationals as against that applied in the International Supreme Championship shows the difference in standard clearly. At each of these important trials—the three Nationals and the International—there are two tests, Singles (one dog) and Doubles (two dogs), but the courses are very different.

In the Singles of a National Championship, five sheep are placed at a point 400 yards away from the handler. The handler sends his dog out, and the dog must gather the sheep and bring them to the handler —a straight fetch from lift to shepherd. The dog must then drive the sheep from the point where the shepherd stands 300 yards over a triangular course and through two gates. Failure to negotiate the gates means a loss of points, and no second try is allowed. The dog must then separate two sheep from the rest within a ring twenty yards in diameter, and he must be in full control of these sheep. That done, he must drive all five into a six-foot square pen, and finally he must separate one sheep from the flock and prevent it from joining the others for as long as the judges think fit. The whole operation from the moment the dog is first sent out to the end must be completed within fifteen minutes.

That may seem stiff enough—the full difficulty cannot, of course, be appreciated without seeing a trial—but it is positively child's play compared with the task set in the International. In this twenty sheep are used. They are divided into two groups of ten, and each group is placed 800 yards from the shepherd and out of sight of the dog. The dog must gather one group and bring them through a gate obstacle in the centre of the field, leave them there and go and fetch the second group, bring them through the centre gate and unite them with the first group. Failure to negotiate the gate with either group entails a loss of points, and no second try is allowed. This first movement completed, the dog must then drive the twenty sheep on a triangular course (as in the Nationals), but now the course is 400 yards long. Again failure to negotiate the gates means a loss of points, and no second try is allowed. This second movement completed, the dog must then bring the twenty sheep into a ring forty yards in diameter, and must then turn back five marked sheep from the flock. (Needless to say, it must be the five marked sheep, *not* five sheep.) This done, the five marked sheep have to be driven into a six-foot square pen. The time allowed for the whole operation is only thirty minutes.

There are similar differences between Doubles in Nationals and the Doubles in the International. Six sheep are used at Nationals, ten at the International. The National course is 400 yards for the gather, the International is 500 yards. At the Nationals the triangular course is 300 yards; in the International it is 400 yards. The time allowed is twenty minutes at the Nationals, and only twenty-five minutes is allowed in the International.

In addition to these Singles and Doubles, there is also a Driving Championship. This is a comparatively new test, and it is, I think, the most difficult of all. The natural inclination of a sheepdog is to bring sheep to the shepherd. To get a dog to drive sheep away from the shepherd and to maintain a straight course while doing so is really the supreme test of training. In Nationals the dog has to drive a flock of twenty sheep for a distance of 400 yards in a straight line from the shepherd, and he is allowed seven minutes in which to do it. That is difficult enough. But in the International Driving Championship the dog has to drive a flock of fifty sheep for 800 yards over a triangular course and negotiate two gate obstacles on the way, and he must do it in ten minutes. The dog that can do that is a champion indeed.

It is, of course, quite impossible at a trial to reproduce the conditions of practical everyday work on the hillside, in the fields or on the road—let alone the emergencies—of the pastoral year. But there can be no doubt that the dogs are very thoroughly tested in such essentials of their work as gathering, shedding, penning, driving and so on, and that these tests also probe to the full such characteristics as pace, stamina, concentration and steadiness, obedience, both at hand and at a distance. One cannot ask more of a trial.

And it must be remembered that, unlike Field Trials for gundogs, the dogs taking part in sheepdog trials are genuine working sheepdogs, working regularly, day in and day out, on the farm. They are not dogs kept specially for the purpose of winning trials. No other sheepdog, even if it were well enough trained, could compete with these working collies; no sheepdog, other than a genuine working dog in full work, would be anything like fit enough to last through a trial. In fact, what these sheep-dog trials have done is to produce a special type of working dog, which can properly be called the British sheepdog, though it is popularly known as the Border Collie.

All the dogs seen at trials nowadays—and this has been the case at least since 1919—are Border Collies or Welsh Collies, and the Welsh Collie, it should be remembered, now carries a predominance of Border Collie blood. Neither breed is recognised by the Kennel Club. These are dogs bred for speed, stamina and brains, and *not* for show. But their fame has ringed the world. So good are they that they have been exported, and are exported, all over the world. It would not be an exaggeration to say that wherever in the world there are sheep to be herded, there you will find some representative of the British sheepdog.

DRAUGHT DOGS

The use of dogs for haulage is confined, and appears always to have been confined, to the northern hemisphere, and especially to Europe and the lands in or bordering the Arctic Circle. Their use for this purpose is as widespread as ever in and around the Arctic Circle, but in some European countries they are now no longer used at all, and in all European countries they are less used now than they were, say, thirty years ago.

In Great Britain, it seems to have been the growth of traffic in the towns, and particularly in London, that was primarily responsible for the law prohibiting their use. But light gigs drawn by dogs could still be seen here and there until mid-Victorian times. The turn-spit, with a dog to turn the wheel, was still in use in Wales in 1870, and water-wheels at wells, the wheels turned by dogs, may have been in use in Wales and Scotland until a few years later. Some of these wheels were

Boxer.

Boston Terrier.

Pyrenean Mountain Dog.

Great Dane.

Bloodhound.

Basset Hound.

Beagle.

Dachshund.

so arranged that the dog could not rest. The wheel was attached to the ceiling and the dog worked inside it, like a squirrel in a cage, so that once the wheel was in motion he was forced to continue running. Normally, however, the dogs were worked in pairs at a wheel which was in line with, and attached to, the spit, which formed the axle of the wheel. There are many stories told of how a dog, hiding to escape his work, would be betrayed by the second dog, who was in danger of having to work overtime.

These 'Turnspit Tykes' were a distinct breed, now—unhappily, for, despite their stultifying work, they were dogs of great character and intelligence—extinct. Jesse [1] describes them as 'extremely bandy-legged, so as to appear almost incapable of running, with long bodies and rather large heads. They are very strong in the jaws and are what is called hard bitten. They generally have one eye black and the other white. Their colour varies, but the usual one is bluish grey spotted with black. The tail is usually curled over the back.' Queen Victoria, who was a great dog-lover, had three 'Turnspit Tykes' as pets at Windsor at one time.

Dogs are still used extensively for hauling loads in Belgium, Holland, France, Switzerland and Germany, usually for drawing the vans of milkmen and bakers. We, in Britain, are inclined to regard this practice as extremely cruel, though we do not, strangely enough, object to the British Antarctic Expedition using dogs for drawing heavy loads (even in an age that has invented the snow-cat), nor regard the Canadians as cruel for making habitual use of them in their Arctic provinces. Let it be said at once that there is no cruelty whatever attached to the practice. It is true that in England in the old days there was sometimes considerable ill-treatment of draught dogs, but there is none on the Continent. In Belgium, Holland and Switzerland particularly great care is taken to ensure that there should be none; there is a rigorous system of inspection of dogs, their harness and their vehicles, and laws regulate the weight of the loads that may be drawn by single dogs, by pairs and by teams.

In Europe proper the dogs used for haulage are all cross-breds with a strong strain of Mastiff. In Canada, Russia and the Arctic countries generally the dogs used are all of the Spitz family, and are mostly Huskies in Canada and Alaska, and Laikis in Russia and Siberian Russia. In both Canada and Russia trials are held of working dogs with a view to improving speed and stamina. The great Canadian event is

[1] *Researches into the History of the British Dog.*

the Dog Derby, but better known, perhaps, is the All-Alaska Sweepstakes. This is a sled race for teams of Huskies over a set course of 420 miles, the event lasting five days. Russian trials are, I believe, even more severe, both in the load hauled and in the distance covered.

WAR-DOGS

The use of dogs in war goes back, at least, to the great civilisations of the Middle East; to the empires of Assyria, Babylon and Egypt. And dogs have been used in war ever since and all over the world. Three of the greatest generals in history—Attila the Hun, Frederick the Great and Napoleon—made extensive use of dogs in their campaigns. Frederick the Great, who made a close study of Attila's methods in more ways than one, was very impressed with the value of dogs in warfare, and the Germans have used dogs ever since, becoming remarkably skilled in their training and employment.

We know, from the accounts of Julius Cæsar, that the Britons of his day employed dogs in war on a considerable scale. And their use in this connection appears to have continued until the close of Tudor times. We know that Henry VIII presented the Emperor Charles V with four hundred war-dogs for use in his war against France, and that Elizabeth I provided the Earl of Essex with a hundred war-dogs for use in his campaign in Ireland. But from that time until 1916 the value of dogs in war seems to have been completely forgotten by British military authorities. And this is the more strange since the dogs used by the Russians in the Russo-Japanese War for guarding the Manchurian Railway Line, and the dogs used by the Turks in the Balkan War of 1910 were trained and supplied by a British ex-army officer, Colonel E. H. Richardson.

When the 1914–1918 War broke out, there was not a single dog attached to the British Army, and it was not until 1916 that the War Dog Training School was established. In that war dogs were mainly used by the British as messengers—so much so that the establishment became known as the Messenger Dog Service—and valuable services they rendered. Indeed, so valuable that just before the Armistice orders were issued that infantry battalions in the attack were to be provided with messenger dogs. Yet, as soon as that war was over, the War Dog Training School was abandoned, not even a skeleton staff being maintained. Thus, when the 1939 war broke out we found ourselves in the same position as in 1914. But, if Colonel Richardson had found difficulty in persuading the War Office to take an interest in dogs, the difficulty was immeasurably greater in 1939. Now, it was pointed out that this was a mechanical war (how much the War Office knew about mechanical warfare was to be demonstrated cruelly in 1940), and that for this reason, among many others, dogs could not be usefully employed. This typical attitude of mind was broken down only with great difficulty by Mr. H. S. Lloyd and certain others, and finally, in 1940, the War Office decided that dogs might be of some use, and established a small experimental school with Mr. Lloyd as technical adviser. There were, of course, no dogs; and the public were invited to 'lend' their dogs. Seven thousand were offered in the first two weeks. But it can, with absolute justice, be said that the British Army War Dogs School of the Second World War succeeded in spite of the attitude of the War Office.

Abroad the situation was very different. Germany had not forgotten the example of Frederick the Great. The German Army used dogs with great success in the war of 1870 (the first German Army Dog School was established in 1848), and from then onwards undertook their study and training most thoroughly, holding competitions throughout the country at regular intervals, paying premiums for good stallion dogs, and constantly experimenting with new breeds. As a result, they were as far ahead of their enemies in this department as in all others when the 1914 war broke out, and in this department at least they remained well ahead until the end. Both the Belgians and the French had army-dog schools in being before the 1914 war and both kept them in being afterwards, and the Swiss have used dogs to assist their frontier guards for at least forty years. But next to the Germans, it is the Russians who have gone into this matter most thoroughly. They learned the lesson in the Japanese war and have never forgotten it. The Russians seem to have been the first people to train dogs as mine-detectors, and they were certainly the first to drop dogs with parachute battalions.

The uses of dogs in war are manifold. They have been used for carrying ammunition to positions outside the reach of other forms of transport; as messengers; as Red Cross workers, finding wounded and leading ambulance workers to them; as telephone layers, paying out the cable as they move forward; as patrol dogs, working with reconnaissance parties; as guards; as mine-detectors; and so on. I think that there can be little doubt that Continental nations recognised the dog's ability to perform tasks of this sort so long before we did simply because dogs on the Continent have been used for work for so long, and are still so used by many people. In Britain, for almost a century now, and with very few exceptions, the dog has been regarded primarily as a pet or as a show specimen. But we do appear, at long last, to have learned the lesson, for the Army War Dogs School is still in being.

POLICE DOGS

The work of police dogs springs naturally from their employment in war. It is not, therefore, surprising to find that here, as in war, Britain has lagged behind some Continental nations, and especially the Germans. They are now used in many different ways, but the one which stirs popular imagination is that of tracking. This is, of course, the medieval use and the dog then used was the Bloodhound. The Bloodhound was also the breed most commonly used in the United States and in Cuba for the recovery of escaped slaves. It is still used to-day, and more than one county constabulary has its kennel of bloodhounds. Though we have been brought up to regard the Bloodhound as an infallible tracker, modern conditions weigh heavily against its success except on a really hot trail or in open and comparatively unfrequented country. Other, and less publicised, uses are of much greater value to the police in the preservation of the peace.

RESCUE DOGS

I have already mentioned the work of the Red Cross dog in war. This is the foremost way in which dogs are used in rescue. The training is comparatively simple. All that is necessary is that the dog should learn not to take notice of anyone except people in a prone position, and he can be taught this quickly. Having found such a person, he returns to his handler and sits at his feet. The handler then attaches a lead to his harness and is led to the casualty. An immense amount of invaluable work has been done by these trained dogs, particularly, of course, in war.

But a word must be said here about the legend of the St. Bernard; a legend which has gained world-wide acceptance as fact, and which has now been immortalised by a delightful advertisement for one of the better known brandies. The St. Bernard is popularly supposed to have been bred at the monastery since the time of the saint (1081). There is not one word of truth in this. And the dog is also popularly supposed to spend its time in winter digging in the deep snow-drifts on the pass, finding lost travellers, and then pouring cognac down their throats. There is not a word of truth in this either. There is no mention of dogs in the records of the hospice before 1774, and a glance at the massive build of the St. Bernard and its thick coat should be quite sufficient to convince anybody that no breed could be less fitted for work in heavy snow. The dog would sink into the snow, its thick coat would soon become clogged, and the animal would be rendered helpless in a matter of minutes. The St. Bernard was, in fact, used not to rescue travellers in the depth of winter—there were, in any case, remarkably few—but to guide the monks on their way down or up the pass; it being realised that the dog would not, on any account, walk into deep snow and that, therefore, where the dog would tread, man could also tread with safety.

GUIDE-DOGS

At the end of the First World War the German Government presented each of their war-blinded soldiers with a fully-trained guide-dog. Just as they had led the world in the training of dogs for war, so now they led the world in the training of the dog for the most humane purpose of all, and for this they must be given full credit. This German movement was so successful that other countries soon adopted the idea, and began to train dogs for guiding blind people. The first to do so were the Swiss, the movement—known as L'Oeil Qui Voit—being started by an American lady, Mrs. Harrison Eustis. Italy and France soon followed suit. In Britain, the Guide-dogs for the Blind was founded in 1930, and Captain Nikolas Liakoff is the chief trainer. The movement spread to the American continent very shortly afterwards.

The training of guide-dogs varies a little from country to country, but the underlying principles are the same the world over. First of all, the dog for training has to be selected with great care. It must not be too large, for if it is the man will be unable to control it at all; it must not be too small, for small dogs have rapid acceleration, and this would make life impossible for the blind man. It must not be nervous, for a nervous dog is easily frightened and in fear will forget everything. It must not be suspicious, for a suspicious dog will cower and shrink, hide behind his master instead of leading him. It must not be aggressive, for obvious reasons; but it must have strong protective instincts—what is technically known as protective aggression. Equally, since the dog is, in fact, in charge of the man, it must be powerful enough to impose its will if need be at moments of crisis. Above everything else, it must be willing. For it cannot be too strongly stressed that the training of a guide-dog differs from the training of all other dogs, for whatever purpose, in this : that the training is only a preliminary, a basic grounding. From the moment that the dog passes into the ownership of the blind person, training begins afresh, both for human and dog, and continues for the rest of their lives. Each, for the rest of life, must continually be making adjustments.

Now, only a limited number of breeds have been found to approach these requirements. These are Alsatians, Border Collies, Keeshonds, Labradors and Boxers, though a certain number of crossbred sheepdogs have been used. Most of these breeds have drawbacks. Boxers are, as a general rule, much too phlegmatic. Border Collies, though very easy to train, are often a little too quick in their movements. Labradors are usually lacking in initiative. The coat of the Keeshond requires much more grooming than the average blind person is able to give, and the dogs themselves are a little small. Only the Alsatian (the German Shepherd-dog) has proved ideal. This was the first breed to be used, and to-day at least ninety-five per cent. of the guide-dogs in the world are Alsatians. Of the remaining five per cent. the vast majority are Border Collies, though there is, I understand, an increasing use of Dobermann Pinschers in the United States.

Only bitches are used as guide-dogs, of course. They are less liable to distraction, less liable to quarrel with other dogs, and seem to have, naturally, a greater sense of responsibility. This is certainly the case with the Alsatian bitch. The Alsatian is very amenable to training and is thoroughly trustworthy, and, being a sheepdog, is full of initiative. Lack of initiative, which is a common fault in gundogs, is a fatal handicap in a guide-dog, which must many times every day give orders to her owner. The sort of 'intelligence' which makes for a first-class Obedience Trial dog does not make for a good guide-dog.

The period of basic training necessary for a guide-dog is about four months. After that time the blind person must go to the training establishment and be trained with the dog. This is absolutely essential, since there must be perfect understanding between human and dog. During this three-week period, the dog gets accustomed to her new owner, who grooms and feeds her each day, and the blind person is instructed in the use and treatment of the dog. Though actual methods of training may vary a little from counry to country, this practice is universal. In England, at the time of writing, it costs about £250 to train a guide-dog.

VII

THE DOG BECOMES BIG BUSINESS

THE first recorded dog show was held in Newcastle in 1859. It was promoted by a local sportsman, a Mr. Shorthose, in partnership with a local gunsmith, a Mr. Pape, who presented the prizes—sporting guns of his own manufacture. There were only fifty entries, all sporting dogs (twenty-three Pointers and twenty-seven Setters), but among the judges was Dr. J. H. Walsh ('Stonehenge'), and this was sufficient to arouse considerable interest. A number of other dog shows were held in that year, the most important of which was a Foxhound Show, promoted by the Cleveland Agricultural Society, and held at Redcar. This may be considered the forerunner of the now famous Peterborough Show.

In the same year the National Dog Show Society was formed to promote a show which was to be held in Birmingham annually in the autumn. The Birmingham shows continued and grew in popularity, but the National Dog Show Society had a short life. So also had the National Dog Club, which promoted a show at the Crystal Palace, which was such a disastrous affair financially that the promoting club came to an end forthwith.

The first really large dog show was 'The First Annual Grand National Exhibition of Sporting and Other Dogs', which was held at the Ashburnham Hall, Cremorne, Chelsea, from 23rd to 28th March, 1863. This was reported at length in *The Field*:

'A great man struggling under difficulties is said to be one of the grandest sights in creation; and if so the British public must have been highly favoured during the past week; for while it is universally admitted that Mr. E. T. Smith, the "proprietor of the first Annual Grand National Exhibition of Sporting and other Dogs", is a great man (in his way), it is patent to all who have witnessed his labours that he has been overwhelmed by the difficulties of the task which he has undertaken. No doubt, to his comprehensive mind it appeared simple enough to collect together, first a lot of dogs to be seen, and then a mass of spectators to see them; but he had overlooked the fact that these animals must be arranged and provided for in a way that should at once conduce to their health and to the instruction as well as gratification of his guests. To effect these objects there must be some knowledge of the habits of the dog, as well of his varieties; but in both these departments of natural history Mr. Smith and his subordinates seem to be utterly deficient. We should have imagined that no Englishman could be ignorant of the fact that dogs require constant access to water when in confinement; and this element is more especially necessary to their health when they are in the state of excitement inseparably connected with a dog show. An outlay of one penny per dog would have procured the 1,200 occupants of the Ashburnham Hall an earthen pan which might easily have been replenished from the fountain which formed a veritable torture of Tantalus in the middle of the building. . . . As no expense seems to have been spared in decorating the hall or in providing prizes, we cannot suppose that parsimony had anything to do with this omission, and therefore can only attribute it to gross ignorance of the habits of the dog. This opinion is confirmed by the general arrangements, or rather by the absolute want of them, exhibited throughout the show. For instance, instead of the intending exhibitors being furnished, as is usually the case, with numbered tickets, to be tied to the collars of the dogs (which is all that is necessary for identification by the proper officials), each dog was labelled with the name and address of the owner, and thus the judges could not avoid knowing the proprietors of the animals they were selecting for prizes. We object to all attempts at "throwing dust in the eyes" of judges; they ought to be men of honour, and above being biased by private friendship. If, however, the public are led into the belief that the gentlemen to whom this onerous task is committed have no means of knowing the ownership

Alsation.

Cardigan Corgi.

Old English Sheepdog.

Collie.

of the dogs they inspect, while all the time they cannot help seeing the name and address on each, a deception is committed which is utterly inexcusable; and no one can be surprised under these circumstances when disappointed exhibitors complain that friends of "the proprietor" are unduly favoured. . . . A worse omission, however, than the absence of water is the crowding of the dogs, without any proper division between them. The Hall itself is capable of properly accommodating 600 dogs on the ground, as we know from having carefully measured its area some years ago, with a view to a dog show then contemplated. But this number can only be safely arranged there by separating each dog in the middle tiers from his fellows by wooden partitions. Such is the plan hitherto pursued at all the previous shows, and experience gained in them has proved that the precaution is necessary, for two reasons: first, because it tends to reduce the excitement caused by near contact with strange animals of the same species; and secondly, because it allows of a much longer chain, since the thin layer of deal permits the adjoining individuals to be within half an inch of each other without their knowledge. . . . Not only has Mr. Smith dispensed with partitions altogether between the dogs in each row, but he has introduced an open wire fence between the rows themselves, thus completely preventing the poor dogs from retreating into a quiet corner in any one direction. In front they have the spectators to guard against, close on each side is an animal of the same variety of the *species canis*, while behind them is another of a separate class, who can express his disgust and contempt in the way most galling to the feelings of the poor brutes, as well as physically disagreeable to their skins. With these special provisions for the discomfort of the dogs, our readers can scarcely be surprised that owners have grumbled loudly and that the services of the veterinary surgeon, who has been appointed since the commencement of the show, have been in constant requisition. . . .

'But Mr. Smith may allege that he has sacrificed the dogs themselves to the advantage of the public: let us see how this plea will avail him. On entering, the spectator was no doubt gratified with the sight of a building admirably calculated for the exhibition of dogs or any other objects of natural history. The main hall is a fine open space, well covered in from the elements, and at the same time sufficiently lighted and ventilated; but the new wing, specially built for the toy and pet dogs, certainly does no credit to the supervision of Messrs.

Brown and Gilbert, who have long been announced as taking this department under their fostering care, for, from the nature of its roof (of glass), it is sure to be either too warm or too cold. Indeed, when we first entered it on Monday, under a glaring sun, it was hot enough to produce hydrophobia, especially in the absence of water to which we have already alluded. . . . Beyond this every arrangement was as bad as possible. To find any particular specimen was a long task, and, in many cases, when the proper number was reached, either the animal indicated in the catalogue was absent, or it was misplaced in the wrong class, or it did not correspond at all with the description. Thus, among the setters (Class 19), No. 229 was a retriever about as fit for a prize as those which obtained them in the proper class, but no doubt overlooked by the judges; while a setter (No. 470) was placed among the Newfoundlands. Mr. Riley's bitch retriever and puppies, which had been thought worthy of a prize at previous shows, had no number at all affixed to her pen, and most probably escaped the notice of the judges altogether, being displaced from her proper class. Among the foreign dogs confusion reigned pre-eminently; five or six had no numbers attached, and a lot of puppies occupied the bench allotted to No. 1195, which is described in the catalogue as "Wolf, brought from the Crimea". A couple of the Dachshund—a foreign variety of great interest to many sportsmen—were neither labelled nor inserted in the catalogue; and in another pen we caught sight of two Japanese dogs, which were neglected in the same way. Our enquiries from the attendants as to these omissions resulted in no useful information, nor could we discover, either from Mr. Barrett or Mr. F. Brailsford, on what principle the classification was adopted. . . . So ignorant of the want of arrangement were these officials, that the former told us that the large non-sporting dogs would be found around the walls of the hall while the rows of benches down the middle were occupied by sporting dogs. Here we thought we had found some clue to the maze in which we had previously been wandering, but alas! our hopes of lightening our labours were soon damped, for we found that the occupants of the walls were first bloodhounds (sporting), then mastiffs (non-sporting), next deerhounds belonging to the first division, and after these collies, included in the second; and so on all round, while in the middle tier the bulldogs and Dalmatians contended for notice among pointers, setters, retrievers, and spaniels. . . . The visitors on the first day could gain no information as to the prizes; for, though the judges had nearly completed their labours on Saturday, no prize list was published, nor was a single prize ticket appended when we left at four o'clock on Monday. A general opinion was expressed that the "screw was being applied" to change the verdicts of the judges in certain cases; but this of course was only a *canard*, although we do happen to know that the statement of a judge as to his selection in one class, made to us on Monday, did not correspond with the prize list as it appeared on the following day. He may have made a mistake, but it is very curious if it was so, as we had a long discussion on the merits of the very animals concerned. In this particular case we have no reason to complain, as the change, if really made, was in accordance with our expressed opinion....'

The correspondent of *The Field*—and no one familiar with the style of 'Stonehenge' can doubt that it was J. H. Walsh—then went on to consider the various classes and individual dogs thoroughly and from the point of view of an expert.

This slashing report has been quoted at some length, because there can be no doubt that it had a great effect on all subsequent dog shows, and no doubt also that it sowed a seed in the minds of certain influential persons, the seed which ten years later was to blossom into the foundation of the Kennel Club.

But it must not be thought that dog shows immediately became standardised and efficient. One has only to scan the columns of *The Field* in the years immediately following the publication of this report to realise that the promoters had taken note of the warning and were much more careful in their arrangements, both with regard to the judging and in the well-being of the exhibits. But dog shows were still very free-and-easy affairs, and it is evident from the study of early catalogues that the exhibitors were allowed to say pretty well what they liked when describing their dogs. This was but one of a number of very undesirable practices.

However, a number of important dog shows were held at the Crystal Palace in the late sixties and early seventies under the guidance of an influential committee. It was one of the members of this committee, S. E. Shirley, who founded the Kennel Club in 1873, finding the nucleus for its membership amongst his fellow committeemen. Within two months of its foundation the Kennel Club was holding a show at the

Crystal Palace, and I think it may be said that this first Kennel Club Show was really the start of the modern show movement.

Realising the importance of having pedigrees available, the Kennel Club immediately set about the compilation of a Stud Book. The first volume of the *Kennel Club Stud Book* was published in 1874. Consisting of 600 pages, it contained the pedigrees of 4,027 dogs, divided into forty breeds and varieties, and including the principal winners at the leading shows up to that date. It also contained 'a code of rules for the guidance of dog shows as well as for the manner in which field trials should be conducted'.

One of the first rules—and certainly the most salutary—framed by the new club was that which required that before a dog could be exhibited at a show held with the approval of the Kennel Club, it must be registered with the Club under a distinctive name. This was essential in order to establish, so far as possible, the identity of a dog and to prevent it being shown in classes for which it was not eligible. This was a quite common form of trickery at all the early dog shows; indeed, it was not uncommon for one dog to be exhibited under several different names, and sometimes even under the names of different owners.

As might be expected, the new Club and its rules were not universally welcomed at the outset. In particular, the rule about registration met with considerable opposition, and especially from the Birmingham Show Committee. This Committee was a very influential body with much more than a merely local reputation, and it did not relish seeing its thunder stolen. Its opposition was fierce and sustained, and at one time it seriously considered publishing a Stud Book of its own. But finally, in 1885, an amicable arrangement was reached, whereby the Birmingham Dog Show Society became entitled to send two delegates to sit upon the committee of the Kennel Club.

To begin with, of course, not all shows were held with Kennel Club approval. Plenty were held without it, and until 1881 particulars of winners at these shows were published in the *Kennel Club Stud Book*. In 1882 the Kennel Club decided not to recognise shows that were held without their approval, and not to publish details of them in the Stud Book.

Four years later, in 1886, Charles Cruft held his first dog show. Charles Cruft was a man of immense personality, a tireless worker and a born showman. The son of a jeweller, he was born in London and educated at a private school at Shoreham. 'Educated' is, perhaps, too strong a word, for by the time he was fourteen he had become bored with academic pursuits and had taken a job as assistant in James Spratt's shop in High Holborn. This was in the year 1866. James Spratt had not been baking his biscuits (then known as 'dog cakes') for very long, and the business was only just starting to expand. Spratt spent most of his time supervising the production of his biscuits (which were made to his own recipe), and it became Cruft's business to sell them and to help with the book-keeping. It soon occurred to him that the best way of selling them would be to visit dog-owners up and down the country, and persuade them personally. Contact with dog-owners soon convinced him that the most likely people to buy dog foods in quantity were those who took a real pride in their dogs, and so he set about helping in the promotion of shows and in the foundation of canine societies. He soon gained a considerable reputation as a virile and efficient organiser. But, curiously enough, his first major experience in the management of a dog show was gained in France. In 1878 he was placed in charge of the dog section of the great Paris Exhibition. He turned what was originally intended to be no more than a sideline into a tremendous success. He was, in fact, already a man of stature in the dog world when he promoted his first show in London.

The title page to this event bore the following statement:

> 'Catalogue and award of prizes of the First Great Show of all kinds of Terriers held at the Royal Aquarium, Westminster, Wednesday, Thursday and Friday, March 10th, 11th and 12th, 1886. Patrons: Gen. Lord Alfred Paget; Maj.-Gen. Raines, C.B.; C. I. Hensley, Esq.; C. G. Cresswell, Esq.; T. H. Bolton, Esq., M.P. General Manager: De Pinna, Esq.'

The show attracted 273 exhibitors and 570 entries, divided among 57 classes. All the dogs, except those in the selling and novice classes, were registered at the Kennel Club.

In 1890 a move was made to the Central Hall, in Holborn, and collies and several breeds of toy dogs were added. (Cruft was always very interested in the toy breeds; he had been secretary of the Toy Spaniel Club and of the Pug Dog Club, and also secretary of the Toy Dog Show.) For this show there were 1,510 entries, divided among 220 classes, and the prizes were worth £1,200. This was the first show at which Charles Cruft presented his own cups, four in number, known as the Cruft Challenge Cups. These Challenge Cups were valued at twenty-five guineas each, and an interesting condition was attached to their presentation: 'An exhibitor winning one of these Cruft Challenge Cups shall not be entitled to have it in his possession unless he has previously deposited with the said Charles Cruft the sum of £25.' Mr. Cruft, a shrewd judge of character, evidently had not a high opinion of the honesty of some exhibitors.

In the following year, 1891, the show was moved to the Royal Agricultural Hall, which was to be its home, with the exception of the years 1918–1920, until 1939. This was the first occasion on which it was announced as Cruft's Great Dog Show. The advertisements—Charles Cruft was always very much alive to the value of advertisement—proclaimed that it consisted of 'the largest number and the finest collection of dogs ever brought together. Every breed represented. Dogs from all parts of the world.' There were, indeed, 2,000 dogs in the hall, and no fewer than 473 classes. There were, moreover, entries sent by the Queen and the Prince of Wales, and the Queen won first prize and cup in the open class for Collies.

The move to the Royal Agricultural Hall was a bold venture. It could only have been taken after deep thought, and it must have required great courage to take a step of such magnitude. But it was the decisive step in the career of Charles Cruft. The first show at the Royal Agricultural Hall received great publicity, partly, of course, because of the entries by the Royal Family and the success of the Queen. And this publicity was not confined to Great Britain. The show began to be talked about on the Continent and in America. Queen Victoria and the Prince and Princess of Wales continued to be frequent exhibitors, and in 1893 the Czar of Russia sent over a magnificent team of eighteen Borzois. Charles Cruft was always extraordinarily successful in persuading foreign breeders and owners to exhibit their dogs, and in securing the services of foreign experts to judge them. There can be no doubt that his early experience of foreign shows, and the honours—such as the gold medal of the Société St. Hubert à Bruxelles—which were conferred upon him, stood him in good stead in this respect.

At any rate, the show which had never looked back from its beginning in 1886, began to make enormous strides from its first appearance at the Royal Agricultural Hall. In 1902 there were nearly 3,000 entries; by 1924 they had increased to 4,240. Naturally, during the war they fell off. In 1917 there were no Royal entries, and it was in this year, at the height of the submarine campaign, that doubts were first expressed as to the advisability of continuing the show. Indeed, there was widespread doubt about the wisdom of continuing to feed dogs, and especially the larger breeds, at a time when there was a serious threat that the nation would be starved into submission. In the following year the Kennel Club placed a ban on all breeding activities, and Cruft's Show was not held in 1918, 1919 and 1920.

When it opened again in 1921, the entries numbered only 2,860, but the King entered two Labradors and Queen Alexandra entered a Borzoi. But the end of the war and the lifting of all restrictions brought a tremendous influx of new exhibitors. The entry in 1922 was 4,587 (then a record), and it rose in each of the following years: in 1923 to 5,778, in 1924 to 6,813, in 1925 to 8,188. From then until the Jubilee Show of 1936 the entries never fell below 9,000, and in that year the entries totalled 10,650.

The last show arranged by Charles Cruft personally was that of 1938, when the entries numbered 9,109. It was in this year that King George VI entered two Labradors. Cruft's death, at the age of 87, was a grievous blow to the dog world, here and abroad, but it did not bring the show to an end. Miss Hardingham had joined the organisation in 1925 as personal assistant to Charles Cruft, and she was the secretary and chief organiser of the 1939 show. There was, of course, no show during the war. Shortly after war broke out, Mrs. Cruft decided that she would have to sell the goodwill. She was very anxious that it should not fall into the wrong hands and become a purely commercial promotion, and she approached Arthur Croxton Smith, the Chairman of the Kennel Club. The Kennel Club found the necessary money, and the greatest show of its kind in the world was preserved as its founder would have wished.

I have many personal memories of Charles Cruft. I think that, perhaps, the most memorable thing about him was that, one of the greatest showmen that the world has yet produced, he disliked personal publicity. He would appear at the Show Luncheon, but otherwise he stayed in the background, always accessible, always courteous, always urbane and unmoved, yet always retiring.

It was not possible to restart Cruft's Show until 1948. It was held in October of that year, and Olympia was hired for the occasion. The Royal Agricultural Hall was not available, but even so this was an even bolder step than that taken by Charles Cruft in 1891. Olympia is not an easy hall to fill; so great is the floor space that it has the capacity to make even a large crowd seem small. In the event, however, it was fortunate that Olympia was taken, for more than 50,000 people paid for admission on the two days. The entries numbered 9,412 provided by 4,273 dogs.

The story of the post-First World War years was being retold with emphasis. Once again there was a tremendous influx of new breeders and exhibitors. The figures speak for themselves :

1950. 12,319 entries : 5,720 dogs
1951. 11,265 entries : 5,543 dogs
1952. 12,448 entries : 6,040 dogs
1953. 12,033 entries : 5,865 dogs
1954. 11,835 entries : 5,956 dogs [1]
1955. 11,869 entries : 6,127 dogs
1956. 12,328 entries : 6,433 dogs

The number of dogs entered for the 1956 show constitutes a record for a dog show anywhere in the world, but one which, it seems probable, will be broken in the near future.

The story of the uninterrupted success of Cruft's Show must not be taken to mean that the show world as a whole ran smoothly and successfully from 1886 onwards. That is very far from the case. Though the Kennel Club decided in 1882 not to recognise shows that were not held under their authority, such shows continued to be held. The dual system was very far from satisfactory. It was by no means uncommon for promoters of these shows to default on the prize money, for faked dogs to be shown, and for all sorts of trickeries to be practised to circumvent the rules. Exhibitors who disapproved had no redress.

By the end of the century matters had got so bad that certain exhibitors began to press the Kennel Club to take strong action, suggesting that the Club should insist upon all shows being held under their rules or, if they were not, that exhibitors at unrecognised shows should be barred from exhibiting at those held under the authority of the Kennel Club.

In 1900 the Kennel Club set up a Council of Representatives, which consisted of members nominated by clubs devoted to particular breeds and registered at the Kennel Club. In 1903 this Council submitted a resolution to the effect that all dogs shown under Kennel Club Rules or Licence must be registered. This was a revolutionary proposal, and a

[1] The 1954 show was cancelled because of a strike by electricians at Olympia.

special committee, consisting of seven members of the Kennel Club and seven members of the Council of Representatives, was set up to consider it. This committee agreed, and the resolution was then put to a general meeting of the Kennel Club in 1904, and carried. But it was agreed at the time that Hound Shows should not be classified as 'unrecognised'.

As might be expected, there was at the outset very considerable opposition. But—and sooner than might have been expected—people came to realise that it was a very wise move, that it was a very good thing that all shows should be held under one authority. There can be no doubt that the move did much to increase the popularity of dog shows. Indeed, there can be no doubt whatever that the greatest single step forward in the history of British dogs and dog shows was the founding of the Kennel Club.

The keynote of Kennel Club policy is the system of registration under which a dog must be registered with a distinctive name before it can be exhibited. The date of birth, the names of the parents, and the name of the breeder have to be given on a form, which can be obtained from the Kennel Club. The registration fee is very low; a mere five shillings. But if one or both of the parents are unregistered, then a slightly higher fee is charged. The figures for dogs registered at the Kennel Club annually since the war are of great interest:

1946	110,855
1947	120,183
1948	105,390
1949	106,871
1950	100,433
1951	93,141
1952	79,002
1953	79,347
1954	82,236
1955	90,446

There are now some 2,000 shows held annually in Great Britain under the authority of the Kennel Club. These are divided into Championship Shows, at which Kennel Club Challenge Certificates are offered in all or some breeds;[1] Open Shows, in which there are no

[1] A dog or bitch that wins three certificates under different judges becomes a champion. A gundog, however, must also win at Field Trials or be awarded a qualifying certificate.

restrictions on exhibitors making any entries in such classes as are provided; Limited Shows, which are confined to members of canine clubs and societies, or to exhibitors within specified areas, and so on; and Sanction Shows, which are, by comparison, minor affairs designed to offer opportunity to less ambitious exhibitors and beginners. Needless to say, the standard at Sanction Shows is sometimes very high indeed. Many a great dog and many a famous exhibitor has started at a Sanction Show. The Sanction Show, in fact, though it receives little publicity (save occasionally in the local Press) is the life blood of the show world.

The largest and most important of the Hound Shows is the Peterborough Show. This was inaugurated in 1879, and—except for lapses during the two world wars—it has been held annually ever since. Peterborough is often described as the Mecca of the Foxhunter. This it has never been. It is the Mecca of the Hound Lover, which is not the same thing at all. The average foxhunter to-day is primarily interested in horses and a good gallop, and regards hounds and the fox merely as a means to an end. He or she has little or no interest in hounds, and much more often than not knows nothing whatever of hound work. The good Master of Hounds takes precisely the opposite view. His primary interest is in hounds and hound work, and he regards the horse merely as the best vehicle from which he may watch his hounds at work and, if necessary, help them.

Dog shows, it must be said, have met—and meet—with a great deal of criticism. It is sometimes thought that this criticism applies only to the shows held under the authority of the Kennel Club and not to Hound Shows at all. In fairness, it must be said that even Peterborough comes in for its share of criticism, and from informed people, at that.

It is often said that showing hounds tends to the production of an identical type, irrespective of the sort of country hunted. Another common criticism is that showing must inevitably develop a tendency to breed for looks rather than for looks combined with a proved ability in hunting.

Neither criticism, in my opinion, is in the least justified. To take the second first: no Master of Foxhounds, especially in these days of short-lived Masterships, would dream of breeding hounds solely with a view to achieving success in the show-ring. He simply has not got the time. In any case, the practice of breeding hounds specially for the ring—hounds that are not regularly hunted—is provided against by the rules of the

Peterborough Show. As to breeding for looks rather than for looks combined with a proved ability in hunting, it is too often forgotten that a Master of Foxhounds has got to show sport, and account for a certain number of foxes, or lose his membership.

This brings us to the first criticism: that showing tends to produce hounds of an identical type, irrespective of the sort of country hunted. Here again it is too often forgotten that a Master has got to show sport and kill foxes; which means that he must have hounds suited to his country. The Fell Hound, ideally suited to his countryside, would be as useless in Leicestershire as the Quorn Hound, so ideally suited to his countryside, would be in Cumberland. It is inevitable that individual packs must differ widely from each other if they are to be successful.

It may be said that the Peterborough Show can dictate nothing but fashion. And, of course, one can go on criticising fashion for ever, since fashion is always changing and each generation in turn considers that the *ne plus ultra* has been achieved. Study of the records of the Peterborough Show reveals that there have been periods during which certain packs have swept the board. Each in turn became fashionable. One may criticise these changes in fashion, but they have, in fact, proved most beneficial to the breed of the Foxhound over the years. Each in turn has been the 'blue print' for its age, the blue print from which the working models have been fashioned. Each in turn has seen the blending of certain characteristics through various lines in other packs. And there can be no doubt whatever that the result has been that the average standard of the Foxhound throughout the country has been steadily improved. But there has been no standardisation. Hounds are not of an identical type. And they never will be: not only because each type of country demands its own type of hound, but also because the fashion is always changing. No one pack, no one fashion, retains predominance for long.

It is little realised how magnificently the Foxhound has met changing conditions. And there can be no doubt that the Peterborough Show, with its insistence that only hounds that are regularly hunted may be shown, has played a major part in this. The modern Foxhound works in the face of difficulties quite unknown to his ancestors. He has to work over land lavishly treated with artificial manures and chemical sprays; he has to work in an atmosphere laden with the fumes of oil and petrol. That he can hold a scent under such conditions is miraculous, no less. He has, moreover, to go at a far greater pace than did his ancestors, if he is to keep ahead of the galloping hordes behind him. Finally, modern conditions make much heavier demands upon stamina than did conditions even as recently as thirty years ago.

No matter how beautiful a hound may be to look at, he is useless if he has a bad nose, a silent tongue and no stamina.

It is the justification of Peterborough—nay, it is the triumph of Peterborough—that it has improved type over the years while maintaining all these things.

Can the same be said for the shows held under the authority of the Kennel Club? Can it be said, with truth, that these shows have improved type while maintaining the natural characteristics of the dogs shown? Can it be said, with truth, that they have improved type without losing any of these characteristics?

Here the dog world is sharply divided into two classes: those in favour of dog shows and those not in favour. Any discussion between the two is likely to become acrimonious within a few moments.

It is, it must be admitted, all too easy to criticise dog shows. Not on account of their management—dogs shows to-day are very well managed indeed, and the standard of judging and the fairness of the judges is beyond reproach, and for this the Kennel Club deserve the highest praise—but from the point of view of their effect upon the breeds of dog and also from that of their effect upon the people who show. The reporter who, after visiting a big show, was no doubt exaggerating when he wrote: 'Yesterday I spent the afternoon in a hall seething with ill-will.' But it cannot be denied that there is sometimes jealousy, and that disappointed exhibitors are not always careful to hide their feelings or to control their tongues.

And it is true, I suppose, that there are a few exhibitors, a small minority, who are not over-scrupulous in their methods. The Kennel Club Committee, being well aware of the frailties of human nature, have done their best to guard against the unscrupulous exhibitor. Their *Regulations as to the Preparations of Dogs for Exhibition* run as follows:

> A dog shall be disqualified from winning a prize or from receiving one if awarded at any show (except as hereinafter provided) if it be proved to the committee of the show or the committee of the Kennel Club as the case may be:

1. That any dye, colouring, darkening, bleaching or other matter has been in any way used for the purpose of altering or improving the colour or marking of a dog.
2. That any preparation, chemical or otherwise, has been used for the purpose of altering or improving the texture of the coat.
3. That any powder, oil, greasy or sticky substance has been used and remains in the coat during the time of exhibition.
4. That any part of a dog's coat or hair has been cut, clipped, singed or rasped down by any substance, or that a new or fast coat has been removed by any means except in the following breeds: Bedlington Terriers, Bull Terriers, Collies, Fox Terriers (Wire and Smooth), Kerry Blue Terriers, Pomeranians, Retrievers (Curly-coated), Retrievers (Golden), Scottish Terriers, Sealyham Terriers and Yorkshire Terriers. The old or shedding coat and loose hair may be removed in all breeds.
5. That if any cutting, piercing, breaking by force or any kind of operation or act which destroys tissues of the ears, or alters their natural formation or carriage, or shortens the tail, or alters the natural formation or colour of the dog, or any part thereof, has been practised, or any other thing has been done calculated in the opinion of the committee of the Kennel Club, to deceive, except in the case of necessary operation certified to the satisfaction of the committee of the Kennel Club. Dew-claws may be removed in any breed, and shortening tails of dogs of the following breeds will not render them liable to disqualification: Spaniels (except Irish Water), Airedale Terriers, Fox Terriers, Irish Terriers, Kerry Blue Terriers, Sealyham Terriers, Welsh Terriers, Old English Sheepdogs, Poodles, Toy Spaniels, Yorkshire Terriers, Schipperkes, Griffon Bruxellois, and such other breeds as the committee may from time to time determine.
6. That the lining membranes of the mouth have been cut or mutilated in any way.

These are very sound and sensible rules. Their wording is admirably lucid and their meaning absolutely clear. Only the deliberately dishonest can find loopholes in them. There is much money to be made in the modern dog world, and success in the show-ring is the surest way of making it. No doubt the temptation to try to circumvent the rules is great. That only a small minority of the thousands who exhibit dogs each year should attempt to do so speaks very highly for the probity of the general run of exhibitors.

This does not, of course, mean that the general run of exhibitors show their dogs in their natural state. In no show of livestock anywhere in the world is the animal shown in its natural state. One has only to consider the appearance of cattle at the Dairy Show and that of cattle in the fields, of sheep at the Royal Agricultural Show and sheep in the fields, of cats at the National Cat Club Show and the cat about the home, even of budgerigars at the Cage Birds Show and the budgerigar in the living-room, to realise the truth of that statement. The art of showing has been described as the art of deception. In a sense this is true. All the animals exhibited in a show have been beautified to the utmost of their owners' capabilities in this direction. Every exhibitor does his or her utmost (within the rules) to disguise such blemishes as her animal may be unfortunate enough to possess. There is all the difference in the world between this and deliberate faking.

The other main line of criticism—that dog shows have ruined certain breeds in one way or another, but chiefly by destroying their natural characteristics—is more difficult to answer. Indeed, in the case of some breeds it cannot be denied.

It cannot be denied, for example, in the case of the Bulldog and, though to less extent, in that of the Dachshund. Both are achondroplasic breeds; that is, both have achondroplasia, which is a congenital disease of the growing bones, in which the cartilage does not develop, resulting in shortening and deformity of the bones. By concentrating on the peculiar achondroplasic traits in the Bulldog, breeders have produced an animal that is a travesty of the old English Bulldog. The exaggeration of the peculiarities in the breed has been done, of course, for show purposes. If it is continued, it cannot but lead to the ultimate extinction of the breed.

Again, it cannot be denied in certain of the working breeds. Consider, for example, the collie. Mr. James A. Reid, then the secretary of the International Sheepdog Society, addressing the Glasgow Agriculture Discussion Society, said :

> 'Primarily Sheepdog Trials were introduced to promote the better breeding and training of Sheepdogs and, therefore, for the important economic end of the better treatment of stock; but . . . they also served to stress the vital importance of working as opposed to mere show-

bench qualities, for, by this time [1873] the Collie of the show-bench, as a rule with but few exceptions, had become, or was fast becoming, a mere commercial commodity with no real claim to the name of Sheepdog so far as working merit went, whether from lack of brains or disuse through lack of training carried on for generations we do not stop to discuss, the explanation being immaterial here and now. The distinction, however, cannot be over-emphasised. For breeders of working Sheepdogs, although their task otherwise is a more difficut one, are free from, and unhampered by, the extraordinary idiosyncrasies of the average owner of a kennel of Show Collies.'

If this was happening as far back as 1873, there can be no doubt about the situation now. There is now a great difference between the appearance of the working Collie and the show Collie. The former has a round, full eye, a nose of moderate length and plenty of room in his head for brains. The show Collie has an excessively long nose, a small eye and practically no room in his narrow skull for brains. Moreover, the show Collie has been bred larger and larger as the years have passed. He would now be too big for work, even if he was mentally fitted for it; which, let there be no doubt about it, he is not.

Consider the Irish Setter, once a great gundog. Since it has become popular on the show-bench, few are to be seen in the shooting field. The explanation is simple enough: all the working qualities have been sacrificed for looks. The Irish Setter, undeniably a beautiful dog, is now too highly strung, altogether too wild and irresponsible, for reliable work with the gun.

Much the same thing is happening with the Cocker Spaniel. Too many are now highly strung and excitable. Moreover, the features which are particularly admired on the show-bench, and which some breeders tend to exaggerate for that very reason, are precisely those which render the dog unsuitable for work in cover. There are many fewer Cockers in the shooting field to-day than there were before the breed became excessively popular on the show-bench. As the dog for the rough shooter, it has practically disappeared.

Consider the Bedlington Terrier. Within my lifetime the Bedlington was a hard workman-like Terrier, with a good straight back and a head not unlike that of a Dandie Dinmont though rather longer. To-day he has a reachy neck and a roached back, with a coat like 'Mary's little lamb'.

There is no need to consider the show Greyhound. Not one of them could live for more than a few yards with a true running dog. Most are no more than caricature of the working dog.[1]

There is no need to continue in this vein. Everyone knows what has happened to the Wire-haired Fox Terrier. The 'extraordinary idiosyncrasies' of the breeders have given it the appearance of a crude wood-carving executed by a moron. It must be many many years since a Fox Terrier champion went to ground. Certainly no modern one could do so.

This dismal story could be repeated for many other breeds. Indeed, there can be no doubt whatsoever that the show-bench has been responsible for the extinction of at least two breeds. I refer to the old English White Terrier and the Black-and-tan Terrier.[2] In the case of the English White Terrier, 'improvement' was responsible : the breed was 'perfected' to death. (One can, I venture to suggest, see the same process at work with certain other breeds at this very moment.) The old English White Terrier disappeared before my time. But I have owned a true Black-and-tan. The breed disappeared—though one may still come across an occasional moderately good specimen in the Oldham area; not pure-bred by any means, but a passable likeness—simply because it was not fashionable with the showmen.

Fashion in the dog world is constantly changing, for no apparent reason. I do not mean, in this connection, changes in popularity among breeds with the general public; that is an excellent thing. I mean fashion in conformation. It would be true to say that no show champion of twenty years ago—certainly in the terriers, and in most other breeds as well—would stand a chance to-day. In the terriers, at least, their heads would be described as 'coarse'; and none of the old champions, so highly regarded so short a while ago, would, of course, be 'standing up on his toes on stiff and useless pasterns'.[3]

That is one side of the picture. But it is not a complete picture, and it is not, therefore, a just one.

[1] 'Treetops Golden Falcon', who was awarded 'Best in Show' at Cruft's, 1956, is a refreshing exception. His appearance must surely have surprised—and encouraged—the judge considerably.

[2] The Black-and-tan Terrier must not be confused with the modern Manchester Terrier, which is sometimes known as the black-and-tan. The old Black-and-tan Terrier was broken haired, a well-built dog, weighing twenty pounds. The modern Manchester, which is uncommon, is smooth-haired.

[3] James Dickie: *The Dog*.

Poodle.

Irish Water Spaniel.

English Setter.

Cocker Spaniel.

The fact is that the working world and the show world have become quite separate and distinct. There are those who will not admit this; there are many more who do not realise it. But that is the fact.

It is true that the show-bench has brought about the extinction of some breeds. It is equally true that once a working breed reaches the show-bench in any number—and certainly when it reaches the show-bench in numbers equal to those working in the field—then it disappears as a working breed. In fact, it disappears as that breed altogether. What is not generally realised is that a new breed, a show breed, is evolved in its place. If it is true that the show-bench has brought about the extinction of some breeds—and there can be no doubt about that—it is no less true that many breeds would have become extinct if it were not for the stimulus supplied by the competition of the show-bench. I do not think that there can be the slightest doubt that showing has saved many many more breeds than it has destroyed.

Whether it has saved them in the right form is a matter of opinion, but not a matter worth discussion in the light of modern conditions.

The modern Wire-haired Fox Terrier is not a working terrier. It is a show breed pure and simple. I do not think that the breeders pretend that it is anything else. At least, I have never heard one so foolish as to suggest that his dogs would be able to go to ground or accompany a hunt in the field, and I have met very few who have even suggested that their dogs are really good ratters. Of course, one may regret the passing of the working Wire-haired Fox Terrier. But this is an urban civilisation, and there is really very little necessity in an urban civilisation for a working Terrier. If one wants a working Terrier, there are plenty to be had; every hunt in the British Isles breeds them. They are not Wire-haired Fox Terriers, it is true, but the man who really wants a working Terrier will not worry about that. What the show world has done is to evolve a breed to suit modern conditions and meet modern demands.

One may regret the passing of the working Irish Setter. Those who have shot over the working Setter (as I have) may not think very highly of the show breed. But what would, in fact, have happened to the Irish Setter if the show world had not evolved the show breed? How many men, in our urban civilisation, shoot over Setters? Left to itself, as a working dog the Irish Setter would by now, in all probability, be extinct.

Some people, who remember Cocker Spaniels who were really 'cocking spaniels', may not think very highly of the Cocker Spaniels they see in town streets nowadays. But how many people really need a working Cocker in these days; how many would have the time to use one properly? Between 1949 and 1955, both years inclusive, 81,653 Cocker Spaniels were registered with the Kennel Club. I wonder how many Cocker Spaniels there would be in the country to-day had the breed remained strictly a working one? What the showmen have done is to produce what is very nearly an ideal dog for modern urban conditions with its stress on the small suburban house. And for this they deserve congratulations, not abuse. They deserve congratulations, too, for evolving from working strains for which there is now little opportunity many other breeds suited to the demands of modern life.

But, though the show-bench breeders have achieved many triumphs in this direction, there are, it must be admitted, some disquieting trends in modern dog breeding. Sometimes, indeed, one is tempted to the conclusion that there is little understanding of the principles of scientific animal breeding. It cannot be too strongly stressed that change for change's sake is not desirable. Britain did not acquire the reputation of being the 'stud farm of the world' by following such a policy. We won that reputation by achieving what we considered to be the best possible—in horses, in cattle and in sheep—and then sticking to that ideal. When improvements are made—as they have been, for example, in dairy cattle—they are made within the framework of the ideal. We have not spent our time in altering the shape of our horses, our cattle or our sheep out of all recognition. And it is because the foreign buyer knows what to expect that we have such a great reputation throughout the world.

Unfortunately, the same devotion to breeding on correct lines has not been apparent throughout the dog world. That it is as possible to attain an ideal—and stick to it—with dogs as it is with horses, cattle and sheep has been shown in the case of the Foxhound, a hound that has been bred with the greatest care and intelligence for well over a century, with the result that we have to-day about as perfect and aristocratic-looking an animal as could be desired. One has only to look at a Foxhound to know at once that he has been bred with scrupulous care for many generations. One has only to compare pictures of the hounds of fifty years ago with those of to-day to realise that such improvements as have been made—and there have been many—have always been made within the framework of the ideal.

Of course, this is true also of many of the show breeds. Even with some of the newer breeds—and here the temptation to produce something different and startling is always greater—there has been a most commendable adherence to first principles. In this context, the Boxer, I think, deserves particular mention, for this is a new breed to the show-bench—the specialist club was founded only twenty years ago, and recognition was granted by the Kennel Club only in 1939—and one that would lend itself easily to distortion. Indeed, there was a tendency a few years ago to exaggerate the slope of the croup, which would have been the first step to degeneration. How well the specialist club has performed its duties, how well aware of the dangers it is, may be seen by the remarkably level, yet remarkably high, standard that prevails throughout the breed.

What does not seem to be generally appreciated by the show-bench world to-day is the value of the dam. Tom Sebright of the Milton, a great expert on the Foxhound, once summed it all up in a single sentence: 'The dam is the secret.' This is not a belief that is widely held among dog breeders. But it is arguable that the virtues of every living creature are derived from the dam; the idiosyncrasies from the sire. What can happen when these idiosyncrasies are allied to the idiosyncrasies of the breeder may be seen all too clearly on the Terrier benches at any show to-day.

VIII

THE CLASSIFICATION OF THE DOMESTIC DOG

THE classification of the domestic dog has always presented great difficulty. The Romans seem to have been the first people sufficiently interested to attempt it. Their experts divided the domestic dog into three classes:

House dogs (*Villatici*)
Shepherd dogs (*Pastorales*)
Sporting dogs (*Venatici*)

And they had three subdivisions for sporting dogs:

War dogs (*Pugnaces*)
Dogs which hunt by scent (*Sagaces*)
Dogs which hunt by sight (*Celeres*)

They did not distinguish further than that, and it may be said that, so far as it goes, it is a good enough classification. It is certainly a great advance on anything that was produced in medieval Europe.

Juliana Barnes is often said to be the first person to classify the domestic dog. In fact, she made no attempt at classification: she merely published a short list of different types. Dr. Caius went further, for he divided the dogs he knew into classes and thought out some wonderful names for them. As had the Romans, he had three main divisions:

> 'A gentle kind, serving the game.
> A homely kind, apt for sundry necessary uses.
> A currish kind, meet for many toyes.'

This was not as exact as the Roman grouping, but Caius divided his three main groups much more thoroughly. His first group was confined to the hunting-dogs, which were divided into two main classes, the *Venatici*, which hunted beasts, and the *Aucupatorii*, which hunted birds. The *Venatici* were composed of :

Terriers (*Terrarius*)
Harriers (*Leverarius*)
Bloodhounds (*Sanguinarius*)

which fall into the Roman group *sagaces* (which Caius names *Sagax*), and

Gazehounds (*Agaseus*)
Greyhounds (*Leporarius*)
Lymers (*Lorarius*)
Tumblers (*Vertagus*)

which correspond to the Roman group *celeres*.

The *Aucupatorii* consist of only three types :

Spaniels (*Hispaniolus*)
Setters (*Index*)
Water spaniels (*Aquaticus*)

His 'homely kind', which he named *Delicati*, contained only one type :

Spaniel Gentle or Comforter (*Meliteus*)

But his 'currish kind' were divided into two groups, the *Rustici* and the *Degeneres*. The *Rustici* were composed of two distinct types :

Shepherds' dogs (*Pastoralis*)
Mastiffs or Banddogs (*Villaticus*)

But Caius seems to have had some doubts about limiting this section to just two types, for he is careful to say that they were known by a number of different names, and lists the following : Keeper's or Watchman's Dog, Butcher's Dog, Messenger or Carrier, Mooner, Water Drawer, Tinker's Cur and Fencer. The *Degeneres* consisted of three types :

Wapps (*Admonitor*)
Turnspits (*Versator*)
Dansers (*Saltator*)

It was this list which formed the basis for Gesner's classification.

Two centuries later Linnæus published the following list of dogs in his famous work of classification :

Faithful dog (*Canis familiaris*)
Shepherd's dog (*Canis domesticus*)
Pomeranian (*Canis pomeranus*)
Siberian dog (*Canis sibericus*)
Iceland dog (*Canis islandicus*)
Great Water-dog (*Canis aquaticus major*)
Hairy Maltese dog (*Canis pilosus*)
Lion dog (*Canis leoninus*)
Little Danish dog (*Canis variegatus*)
Bastard Pug Dog (*Canis hybridus*)
Pug dog (*Canis fricator*)
Bulldog (*Canis molossus*)
Mastiff (*Canis anglicus*)
German hound (*Canis sagax*)
Hound (*Canis gallicus*)
Bloodhound (*Canis scoticus*)
Pointer (*Canis avicularis*)
Barbet (*Canis aquatilis*)
Greyhound (*Canis cursorius*)
Lesser Water-dog (*Canis aquaticus minor*)
Canis brevipilis pyrame
Little Maltese dog (*Canis parvus melitans*)
Spaniel (*Canis hyspanicus*)
Irish hound (*Canis hibernicus*)
Turkish hound (*Canis turcicus*)
Scotch hunting-dog (*Canis graius*)
Rough Scotch hunting-dog (*Canis graius hirsutus*)
Italian greyhound (*Canis italicus*)
Persian greyhound (*Canis orientalis*)
Hairless greyhound (*Canis egyptius*)
Lurcher (*Canis laniaris*)
Boarhound (*Canis fuillus*)
Turnspit (*Canis vertigus*)
Ala (*Canis americanus*)
New Holland dog (*Canis antarcticus*)

Although there is a great increase in number on the dogs listed by Caius, this cannot be termed a classification. Linnæus gave dogs their place in his classification of the animal kingdom, but he did not classify dogs: he listed the breeds known to him.

Buffon, the great French naturalist, made a much more detailed attempt at classification. Indeed, he drew up a genealogical tree of all the breeds known in his day. The chief interest of this is that he assumes all of them to be descended from the shepherd-dog. His argument was that all savage peoples who keep sheep have a sheepdog, therefore the sheepdog must be the original dog. He extends his argument by maintaining that the sheepdog is the most intelligent of all dogs, and must, therefore, have been domesticated earlier than any other. Buffon divided dogs into five main groups:

1. The shepherd-dog.
2. The hound group: dogs with long and smooth pendulous ears.
3. The spaniel group: dogs with pendulous ears covered with long hair.
4. The greyhound group: dogs with pendulous ears, long bodies and long legs.
5. The bulldog group: dogs with pendulous ears, short noses, short compact bodies, and usually short legs.

We may not accept his argument about the shepherd-dog, and we may think that type to-day is somewhat more confused than his grouping would suggest—since dogs are able to breed freely one with another, irrespective of type, group character is difficult to maintain—but it cannot be denied that Buffon's grouping is more or less correct.

The next major attempt at classification came from W. L. C. Martin, an Irishman who was superintendent of the museum of the Zoological Society, writing in *Knight's Weekly Volume* in 1845:

'We now venture to offer the following as an arrangement of the principal breeds into which the domestic dog appears to be resolvable; from this arrangement we exclude the true wild dogs of India and the dingo of Australia, but retain in it such dogs as have reverted to a life of independence, and which may be termed feral:

1. Ears, erect or nearly so; nose, pointed; hair, long, often woolly; form, robust and muscular; aspect, more or less wolfish.

Feral dog of Russia
Feral dog of Natolia
Shepherd's-dog of Natolia
Persian guard-dog
Pomeranian dog
Icelandish dog
Siberian dog
Tschuktschi dog
Esquimaux dog
Hare Indian dog
Black wolf-dog of Florida Indians
Nootka dog
Shepherd dog

2. Ears, narrow, semi-erect or only slightly pendulous; muzzle, produced; jaws, strong; hair, smooth or wiry; limbs, long and vigorous; power of scent, not highly developed:

Ancient German boarhound
Great Danish dog
Feral dog of Hayti
French mâtin
Irish wolf-dog
Scotch deerhound
English greyhound
Italian greyhound
Persian greyhound
Brinjaree dog
Albanian greyhound
Lurcher

3. Ears, moderately large and pendant; muzzle, deep and strong; hair, long and sometimes wiry; form, robust; aspect, grave and intelligent:

Italian wolf-dog
Newfoundland dog
Labrador dog
Alpine dog

4. Ears, moderately large; sometimes very large, pendant; hair, long and fine; muzzle, moderate; forehead, developed; scent, acute; intelligence at a high ratio:

Griffon Bruxellois.

Cairn Terrier.

Staffordshire Bull Terrier.

Bull Terrier.

Smooth Fox Terrier (Old type: illustration by Arthur Wardle).

Smooth Fox Terrier.

Wire Fox Terrier (Old type: illustration by Arthur Wardle).

Wire Fox Terrier.

Spaniel, and fancy varieties
Water-spaniel and varieties
Rough water-dog or barbet
Little barbet
Setter

5. Ears, large, pendant; muzzle, long and deep; nose, large; hair, close; scent, acute; form, vigorous:

Pointer
Dalmatian dog
Beagle
Harrier
Foxhound
Old English hound
Bloodhound
African hound, etc.

6. Ears, moderate, pendant; muzzle, short and thick; jaws, enormously strong; hair, short, sometimes wiry; form, robust; sense of smell, variable:

Cuban mastiff
English mastiff
Tibetan mastiff
Banddog
Bulldog
Corsican and Spanish bulldog
Pug-dog

7. Ears, sub-erect; muzzle, rather acute; jaws, strong; hair, short or wiry; scent, acute; habits, active; intelligence, considerable:

Terrier—smooth or wire-haired
Turnspit
Barbary dog

We do not offer this arrangement, which is essentially the same as we have elsewhere given, as not liable to objections; indeed, so many mixed breeds of dogs of uncertain origin exist, that any attempt to class them under distinct heads would appear hopeless.'

Martin's classification is certainly most original. It seems to have passed unnoticed at the time—fortunately, perhaps, for his peace of mind—and this may have been due to the almost simultaneous publication of *The Breeds of Domestic Animals*, by Professor David Low, who was Professor of Agriculture in the University of Edinburgh. Low divided dogs into four main groups:

1. The *Lyciscan* Group.
   Dogs approaching more or less to the conformation of the common wolf.
   These include the Esquimaux, Samoyeds, shepherds' dogs of wolf type, also the collie. Related to the Lyciscan group but crossed with other groups: the lurcher, the great dog of Newfoundland.
2. The *Vertragal* Group.
   Example, the greyhound, probably bred from some other form of swifter Canidæ, and not the wolf. Related to these, but crossed with the Molossian Group, are the boarhounds, the Irish wolf-dog, the Great Dane and the Dalmatian.
3. The *Molossian Group*
   These dogs are large and resemble more or less the Mastiff. Found in Thibet, the variety stretches to the western limits of Europe. Related to the mastiff is the bulldog and Great Dane, also the St. Bernard. The bloodhound, intermediate between the mastiff and the hound.
4. The *Indigator* Group.
   (*a*) *The True Hound*.—Probably derived from the wild hound of Nepaul, the dog of Beloochistan, the jackal and the hunting Canidæ of Africa.
   (*b*) *The Mute Hound*.—These include the Lymehound, and dogs used by fowlers, such as the pointer, to which is related the setter.
   (*c*) *The Spaniel*.—Probably a mixture of African blood with that of Western Asia and Europe.
   (*d*) *The Barbet or Water-dog*.—A dog of aquatic situations. 'His feet are webbed.' Includes the poodle.
   (*e*) *The Terrier*.—Related to the Lyciscan Group, and its habits seem to connect it with the burrowing Canidæ, and the most probable supposition is that it has been produced by a mixture of jackal or even common fox with domesticated dogs.

This is almost as ingenious as Martin's classification. But it was generally accepted in its day, because Low had a great reputation and because nobody was very interested in the classification of the domestic dog, being quite content to accept the animal and to leave it at that. If it is quite impossible to accept Martin's classification, Low's is, at the least, very difficult to follow. One has some sympathy with Colonel Charles Hamilton Smith's reported comment: 'At least he knows dogs bark.'

Hamilton Smith himself, in his great two-volume work in Jardine's *Naturalist Library*, divided domestic dogs into six groups—the wolf-dogs, the watch-dogs, the greyhounds, the hounds, the cur-dogs, and the mastiffs—but he did not attempt to trace relationship. He regarded the terrier as belonging to the 'cur-dog' group; the sheepdog, the St. Bernard and the Pomeranian as belonging to the 'wolf-dog' group. When it comes to classification, there is, it seems to me, little to choose between Martin, Low and Hamilton Smith.

J. H. Walsh ('Stonehenge'), who had a passionate interest in dogs and a vast knowledge of them, also tried his hand at classification. In his *Manual of British Rural Sports* (1855) he groups dogs in six classes:

1. Those that find game for man, leaving man to kill it. Example, the spaniel.
2. Those that kill game when found for them. Example, the greyhound.
3. Those that find and kill game. Example, the foxhound.
4. Those that retrieve game wounded by man. Example, the retriever.
5. Those that are useful companions. Example, the mastiff.
6. Those that are toys. Example, the King Charles spaniel.

It will be seen that Walsh's classification depends upon the manner in which dogs behave. This is certainly an original idea, but one would have expected something rather better and more detailed from a man of his stature and authority.

Then, in 1878, came Professor Fitzinger's *Der Hunde und seine Racen*. In it he recognised 180 breeds and varieties.[1] By doing so, he brought attempts at classification of the dog to an abrupt halt. It was

[1] To-day it would be possible to list more than 800 breeds and varieties.

to be almost twenty years before anybody else tried, and when Rawdon B. Lee published his classification in 1894, it was found to be simplicity itself. Lee recognised two groups only: Sporting and Non-sporting. His list of breeds is interesting in comparison with those recognised to-day:

SPORTING

Bloodhound
Otterhound
Foxhound
Harrier
Beagle
Basset-hound (smooth and rough)
Dachshund
Greyhound
Deerhound
Borzoi
Irish Wolfhound
Whippet
Pointer
Setters
Retrievers
Spaniels (Irish Water, Clumber, Sussex, Field, English Springer, Welsh Springer, Cocker)
Fox Terriers (smooth and wire)
Irish Terrier
Scotch Terrier
Welsh Terrier
Dandie Dinmont
Skye Terrier
Airedale Terrier
Bedlington

NON-SPORTING

Bulldog
Bulldog (miniature)
Mastiff
Great Dane
Newfoundland
St. Bernard
Old English Sheepdog
Collie
Dalmatian
Poodle
Bull Terrier
White English Terrier
Black-and-tan Terrier
Toy Spaniels
Japanese Spaniels
Pekingese
Yorkshire Terrier
Maltese
Italian Greyhound
Chow Chow
Black-and-tan miniature
Pomeranian
Pug
Griffin
French Bulldog
Elk
Esquimaux
Lhasa Terrier
Samoyed

THE CLASSIFICATION OF THE DOMESTIC DOG

This is the classification which the Kennel Club decided to adopt. For comparison I append the present Kennel Club classification :

SPORTING

Afghan Hounds
Basenjis
Basset Hounds
Beagles
Bloodhounds
Borzois
Deerhounds
Elkhounds
Finnish Spitz
Dachshunds (long-haired)
„ (miniature long-haired, not exceeding 11 lb. for exhibition)

Dachshunds (smooth-haired)
„ (miniature smooth-haired, not exceeding 11 lb. for exhibition)
„ (wire-haired)
Foxhounds
Greyhounds
Harriers
Irish Wolfhounds
Otterhounds
Rhodesian Ridgebacks
Salukis
Whippets

GUNDOGS

English Setters
Gordon Setters
Irish Setters (Red)
Setters (Crossbred)
Pointers
German Shorthaired Pointers
Retrievers (Curly-coated)
„ (Flat-coated)
„ (Golden)
„ (Labrador)

Retrievers (Interbred)
„ (Crossbred)
Spaniels (Clumber)
„ (Cocker)
„ (Field)
„ (Irish Water)
„ (Springer, English)
„ (Springer, Welsh)
„ (Sussex)
„ (Interbred)

TERRIERS

Airedale Terriers
Australian Terriers
Bedlington Terriers
Border Terriers
Bull Terriers
Bull Terriers (miniature)

Cairn Terriers
Dandie Dinmont Terriers
Fox Terriers (Smooth)
Fox Terriers (Wire)
Irish Terriers
Kerry Blue Terriers

Lakeland Terriers
Manchester Terriers
Norwich Terriers
Scottish Terriers
Sealyham Terriers
Skye Terriers
Staffordshire Bull Terriers
Welsh Terriers
West Highland White Terriers
Yorkshire Terriers

NON-SPORTING

Alsatians (German Shepherd-dogs)
Boston Terriers
Boxers
Bulldogs
Bullmastiffs
Chow Chows
Collies (Rough)
Collies (Smooth)
Dalmatians
Dobermann Pinschers
French Bulldogs
Great Danes
Keeshonds
Mastiffs
Newfoundlands
Old English Sheepdogs
Poodles
Poodles (miniature, under 15 inches)
Pyrenean Mountain Dogs
St. Bernards
Samoyeds
Schipperkes
Schnauzers
Miniature Schnauzers
Shetland Sheepdogs
Shih Tzus
Tibetan Terriers
Welsh Corgis (Cardigan)
Welsh Corgis (Pembroke)

TOYS

Black-and-tan Terriers (min.)
Chihuahuas
Griffon Bruxellois
Italian Greyhounds
Japanese
King Charles Spaniels
Cavalier King Charles Spaniels
Maltese
Papillons
Pekingese
Pomeranians
Pugs

It will be seen that the number of breeds has greatly increased during this century. But the classification remains broadly that suggested by Lee; there are still two main groups, but the sporting now has three divisions and the non-sporting two.

Of course, this is a classification which presents a good many difficulties. But from the point of view of the show-bench—and it is designed purely from the show point of view—it is sound and conveniently simple. I do not think it could be bettered.

From any other point of view—and particularly from the naturalist's—it is meaningless and useless. What right, for example, has an 'interbred' or a 'crossbred' in any classification of breeds? If the words have any meaning at all, they indicate clearly that neither is a breed. Again, from the naturalist's point of view, the words 'sporting' and 'non-sporting' are meaningless. It simply is not true that the Basenji is more sporting than the Corgi, that the Dachshund is more sporting than the Boston Terrier, the Rhodesian Ridgeback than the Alsatian. Furthermore, what is regarded as a sporting dog in this country may not be so regarded anywhere else. One may quibble, too, about the classification of Toy Dogs. The Pug, which may stand ten or eleven inches in height and weigh about fifteen pounds, is a toy; the miniature Dachshund, which stands seven or eight inches in height and which must not weigh more than eleven pounds, is not. Size apparently has nothing to do with it; presumably, the Dachshund does not qualify as a toy because it is 'sporting'. But is the miniature Dachshund really more sporting than the Griffon Bruxellois? I should doubt it—indeed, I should deny it, and so, I feel sure, would everyone who has ever owned a Griffon Bruxellois. An additional criticism could be—and, indeed, this has been advanced by Clifford Hubbard in his *Working Dogs of the World*—that there is no separate section for working dogs; they are classified as 'non-sporting'. It is true that the American Kennel Club does classify 'Working Dogs', placing in that category sled-dogs, cattle-herding dogs and sheep-dogs, but it is not a justifiable criticism so far as the Kennel Club's classification is concerned. The Kennel Club does not recognise such working breeds as the Border Collie, the hunt terrier (inaccurately known as the 'Parson Jack Russell' terrier by many people), and the Lurcher (which has every right to be regarded as a breed if recognition is granted to crossbred retrievers and crossbred spaniels); but this is a classification for show-bench purposes only. As such, it is very adequate.

Nevertheless, it cannot satisfy any knowledgeable dog-lover, let alone the expert. It failed to satisfy that great expert and enthusiast, Edward C. Ash. Ash who, though he never suggested that his was a full classification, divided the domestic dog into families as follows:

The Esquimaux family
The Greyhound family

The Dalmatian and Great Dane family
The Sheepdog family
The Water-dog and Spaniel family
The Terrier family
The Mastiff family
The Newfoundland and St. Bernard family

He then added chapters to cover dogs from China and Japan, and the Maltese dog, presumably because he found difficulty in fitting any of these into the families listed above.

This, though a great advance on anything previously put forward, is far from satisfactory. It omits, for example, many of the hounds; neither the Beagle nor the Foxhound is included in this classification, and, though Ash did not pretend that this was a full classification, these are surely astonishing omissions. Again, he places the Bloodhound in the Mastiff family; a step which makes altogether too heavy a demand on credulity. It is strange, too, to find such breeds as the Chow Chow, the Pekingese and the Maltese left stranded, without connections as it were.

The most recent attempt at classification has been made by Clifford Hubbard in his *Dogs in Britain* (1948). Hubbard, one of our leading authorities and a man with a wide knowledge of foreign breeds and varieties, follows Ash in grouping dogs into families. His classification is, as he is careful to point out, tentative, but he suggests the following grouping:

1. *The Greyhound group:* in which he includes Irish Wolfhound, Deerhound, Borzoi, Afghan Hound, Saluki, Greyhound, Whippet, Ca Eivissenc, Italian Greyhound.
2. *The Spitz group:* in which he includes Husky, Samoyed, Chow Chow, Akita, Finnish Spitz, Elkhound, Keeshond, Pomeranian, Schipperke.
3. *The Mastiff group:* in which he includes St. Bernard, Newfoundland, Tibetan Mastiff, Mastiff, Pyrenean Mountain Dog, Dogue de Bordeaux, Bull Mastiff, Bulldog, Boxer, French Bulldog, Pug.
4. *The Sheepdog group:* in which he includes Owtcharka, Old English Sheepdog, German Shepherd-dog, Groenendael, Komondor, Bouvier, Collie, Shetland Sheepdog, Welsh Corgi.
5. *The Spaniel group:* in which he includes Setter, Pointer, Retriever, Clumber Spaniel, Cocker Spaniel, King Charles Spaniel, Papillon.

6. *The Hound group:* in which he includes Foxhound, Otterhound, Harrier, Beagle, Basset Hound.
7. *The Terrier group:* in which he includes Airedale, Welsh Terrier, Lakeland Terrier, Cao d'Agua, Poodles, Truffle Dog, Yorkshire Terrier, Manchester Terrier, Black-and-tan Miniature Terrier.

Hubbard, it must be remembered, is only giving an outline. He could easily have increased the number of examples he gives for each breed, both from British breeds and from foreign breeds, had he wished. Indeed, in a full classification he would, obviously, place all the British breeds.

Hubbard's suggested classification is as great an advance on that put forward by Ash as was Ash's classification on anything put forward previously. As he points out, it would :

> 'absorb the majority of distinct breeds of established type inclusive of the miniatures generally as well as the so-called "Toy" breeds. Japanese and Pekingese, for example, could well enter the Spaniel group, while the diminutive Griffon Bruxellois would join its fellow miniatures, the Yorkshire Terrier and the Black-Tan Miniature Terrier, in the Terrier group : after all, each Toy is but a small edition of a member of one or another of the above groups.'

In this he is absolutely correct. Any worth-while classification of the domestic dog must absorb the 'Toys' in one or another of the different groups or categories. You cannot classify dogs by size. (Obviously, when it comes to judging in the show-ring, it is necessary to separate them, to some extent, by size; but (as I have shown) even the Kennel Club Committee has not been very successful in this respect.) In this, as in many other ways, Hubbard's classification is much to be preferred to that suggested by Ash.

But even so, it is not wholly satisfactory. I find it, for example, impossible to accept the Poodle as a Terrier, and I do not think that I shall be alone in this. And again, I find it impossible to accept the Truffle Dog as a Terrier—unless, maybe, as a Terrier (crossbred)! Indeed, I find it impossible to accept the Truffle Dog as a breed. I have lived in truffle country almost all my life. Those Truffle Dogs that I have seen at work in England—and I have seen a good many in the past forty years or so, both those of the Collins family and those used by one or two gypsy families—have all been mongrels. One or two may have had a predominance of terrier blood—one, in fact, was described, proudly if inaccurately, by its owner as a Fox Terrier—but not one of the rapidly diminishing number of Truffle Dogs in Britain (I should doubt if there are now more than half a dozen all told) can truly be described as anything but mongrel. Furthermore, in England (contrary to the custom in France), Truffle Dogs have never been specially bred for the job; they have been trained to it.

Nevertheless, Hubbard's classification, though open to criticism, is by far the best yet advanced. Indeed, I do not think that its broad outline is now likely to be improved upon. No classification of the domestic dog will ever be wholly satisfactory, for the simple reason that no fully detailed classification is now possible. The plasticity of the dog, its ability to breed freely one with another irrespective of type, and the whims of breeders in 'manufacturing' new varieties by selection, crossing and so forth, puts a detailed classification out of the question.

One must be content with a broad outline, knowing full well that whatever one suggests within that outline will be subject to criticism. Convinced that Hubbard's outline grouping is by far the best, I follow it in the next chapter. But, just as Hubbard reduced the number of Ash's families and, where he thought it necessary, rearranged their members, so I, while retaining the number of Hubbard's groupings, have on occasion rearranged their members.

IX
THE BREEDS IN BRIEF

THE breeds listed, and briefly described below, are those which are to be found in some numbers in Great Britain to-day. Included are one or two breeds which are not officially recognised by the Kennel Club; where this is so, the fact is clearly indicated. The weights given are those which are considered ideal by show standards. It may be taken that a working dog in hard condition—for example, retrievers and spaniels used regularly in the shooting field—would weigh a couple of pounds or so less than the exhibition dog.

THE SPITZ FAMILY

This is the 'Esquimaux' family of Ash. Since the majority of its members have nothing whatever to do with the Eskimo, I think, with Hubbard, that Spitz is the better name. The family is the most easily recognised of all the canine groups, being distinguished, in general, by a broad skull with a pointed muzzle, sharp pointed ears which are carried erect, and the tail carried curled over the back. The better-known members have a thick, rough coat of medium length. Because of this it is commonly said that the family is confined to northern latitudes. There are, in fact, many representatives of the family to be found in the Middle East and even farther south, and these, while conforming to the family type, have smooth coats.

The Chow Chow. The breed is mentioned in Chinese literature of about 2000 B.C. It was first mentioned as being in England in 1789 by Gilbert White, but was probably introduced earlier. The breed is too well known to warrant description: the black tongue and straight hocks are characteristic. Chow Chows are dogs of marked personality, strongly individual in character, and quite exceptionally loyal to the family with whom they live, while devoted to the one member of that family whom they honour with their affection. Coat: abundant, dense, straight and stand-off; outercoat coarse in texture, undercoat soft and woolly. Colour: whole coloured red, black, blue, fawn cream or white. Height: 18 in. plus. Weight: 55–65 lb.

The Finnish Spitz. Used by the Lapps as a hunting-dog for bear, elk and other big game, and also as a 'bird' dog, in which capacity it acts as a pointer and is very efficient. In this country, to which it was introduced in 1927, it is purely a pet and an exhibition dog. The head is medium sized with a clearly defined stop and a narrow tapering muzzle. The body is almost square with a short straight back and a deep chest. Coat: short and close on head and legs, longer and stiffer on body, forming a ruff on the shoulders; undercoat short and dense. Colour: reddish-brown on back, paler below. Height: 17–19 in. Weight: about 33 lb.

The Samoyed. First introduced by E. Kilburn Scott in 1892. The name comes from a nomadic Siberian tribe from whom Mr. Kilburn Scott obtained his first dog. In Russia the breed is known as the Laika. This is the most beautiful of the Spitz family, and a strong and active dog. The powerful head is wedge-shaped with a broad, flat skull and tapering muzzle. The back is medium in length, broad and very muscular, and the chest broad and deep. Coat: thick, close, soft and short undercoat with harsh hair growing through it to form the overcoat, which stands straight away from the body and is free from curl. Colour: pure white, white-and-biscuit or cream. Height: 20–22 in. Weight: 45–55 lb.

The Elkhound. In its native Scandinavia the Elkhound is used for hunting bear and elk, but also in the shooting field, where it points birds and also makes an excellent retriever. Introduced about 1880, and has since become moderately popular. The head is broad between the ears with a clearly marked stop and a moderately long tapering muzzle. The body is compact and short-coupled with a wide straight back and a broad deep chest. Coat: thick, abundant, coarse and weather resisting, forming a ruff about the neck and chest; undercoat soft and woolly. Colour: grey of various shades with black tips to the long outer coat, paler on the chest, stomach and legs. Height: 19–21 in. Weight: 43–50 lb.

The Keeshond. A breed frequently mistaken for the Elkhound by the uninitiated. First introduced in 1920, and first registered as the 'Dutch Barge Dog'. The name, by the way, should be pronounced 'Kase-hond'. The breed has never, I think, been used for sport, but was at one time commonly used as a draught dog in Holland and Germany. The head is wedge-shaped, broad between the ears, with a tapering muzzle and a definite stop. Coat: dense and harsh, standing away from the body, with a dense ruff and well-feathered legs; the undercoat soft and thick. Colour: ash-grey. Height: 17–18 in. Weight: about 35 lb.

The Schipperke. First introduced in 1887 as the 'Belgian Barge Dog'. This breed is often not recognised as a Spitz because the tail is commonly docked and the coat smooth. When an undocked specimen is seen—and there are plenty on the Continent, though none here—the family relationship is unmistakable. The head is broad between the ears with but little stop, the muzzle medium in length and tapering. The back is short, straight and strong, and the chest deep and broad. The dog has a compact, muscular appearance. Coat: abundant, dense and harsh, smooth on the head and lying close to the back and flanks, but standing erect and thick round the neck, forming a mane. Colour: black. Height: 12 in. Weight: 12–16 lb.

The Basenji. First introduced by Mrs. Burns in 1934, and widely known as the 'barkless dog'. The breed comes from Africa (an example of the southern distribution of the Spitz family), and may have been represented in Egyptian art of 5,000 years ago. There are naturally some differences (other than the smooth coat) from the normal Spitz type due to geographical distribution, but the family relationship is unmistakable. The head is broad between the ears with a tapering muzzle, and the body short-coupled and level with a deep chest. Coat: short and silky. Colour: chestnut with white points, black, white-and-black, tan-and-white. Height: 16–17 in. Weight: 22–24 lb.

The Pomeranian. When first introduced in the seventeenth century weighed 20–30 lb. A miniature variety appeared in the nineteenth century (apparently by mutation not by selective breeding). The small dog became a great favourite with Queen Victoria, and so immensely fashionable. There has been some falling off in popularity during recent years. A typical Spitz with wedge-shaped head and short-coupled compact body. Coat: long, harsh and perfectly straight, very abundant on neck, shoulders and chest, forming a ruff; undercoat soft and fluffy. Colour: all whole colours. Height: not important. Weight: 4–5½ lb.

THE GREYHOUND FAMILY

This is the family of 'running dogs', animals built for speed. They may easily be recognised by their 'tucked up' loins, long, sharp-pointed muzzles, and the general suggestion of swiftness in their long, lean bodies.

The Greyhound. In colour, greyhounds may be black, white, red, blue, fawn, brindle or any of these colours broken with white. There is, as a rule, a marked difference between the show greyhound and the coursing or track dog, show greyhounds tending to be heavier but less finely muscled. Height between 26 and 30 in. Most coursing dogs weigh between 50 and 60 lb. (but 'Swinging Light', twice winner of the Waterloo Cup, weighed 78 lb.); track dogs seem to be getting a little heavier and now average between 60 and 63 lb. Show dogs are rarely much below 70 lb.

The Afghan Hound. First introduced in 1894, first exhibited in 1907. The Afghan is a typical greyhound, save that the coat is fine and short on the back, very long on ears, legs and hindquarters. There is a distinct silky top-knot on the head. Any colour is permissible. Height: 27–29 in. Weight: about 64 lb. There is a tradition that Afghan Hounds were the two dogs taken by Noah into the ark.

The Saluki. May have been introduced as early as Stuart times, but first recognised in 1922. One of the oldest breeds in the world and a typical greyhound in build, but coat smooth and silky with slight feathering on legs and back of thighs. Colour: white, cream, fawn, golden, red, grizzle-and-tan, black-and-tan. Height: 23–28 in. Weight: 50–55 lb.

The Borzoi. The most strikingly handsome of the greyhounds. First introduced in 1872. In Russia, before the revolution, was used for hunting wolves. In England the Borzoi is purely a show animal. Coat: long and silky, short on head, ears and front legs, chest well feathered and tail long with profuse feathering. Colour: white, or white with lemon, orange, red or blue markings. Height not less than 29 in., but may be as much as 34 in. Weight: about 60 lb.

The Deerhound. Also known as the Scottish Deerhound. Now very uncommon. Coat: harsh, wiry and shaggy and about 4 in. long. Colour: dark blue-grey or brindle appear to be the most favoured colours, but any colour, except white, is allowed. White markings are permissible. Height: not less than 30 in. Weight: 85–105 lb.

The Irish Wolfhound. This is the largest British breed. Now very uncommon. Coat: rough and hard, especially wiry and long over the eyes. Colour: grey, brindle, red, black, fawn, pure white. Height: not less than 31 in., but usually 33–34 in. Weight: not less than 120 lb.

The Whippet. A breed that is not more than a century old. Native to the north of England. Recognised in 1895. In appearance a small greyhound. Quite exceptionally fast over a straight course of up to 200 yards. Colour: any colour or mixture of colours. Height: about 18 in. Weight: about 20 lb.

The Italian Greyhound. This is the miniature, the 'toy', of the family. In appearance a tiny whippet. Has been in England since, at least, Tudor times. Coat: thin and glossy like satin. Colour: fawn, white, cream, blue, black, black-and-fawn, and white pied. Height: about 10 in. Weight: 6–8 lb.

The Lurcher. Not recognised by the Kennel Club. Best known as the gypsy's dog, but known in England by this name since medieval times. Breeds true. In appearance a typical greyhound. Coat: short and harsh. Colour: any colour, but black or brindle preferred by gypsies. Height: about 26 in. Weight: 60–70 lb.

THE HOUND FAMILY

These are the hounds that hunt by scent. Hounds may generally be recognised by their long skulls, domed on top and of good breadth; their ears set low and pendant; their great depth of chest in a medium to long body, and their heavily boned and muscled legs.

The Beagle. This is probably the oldest indigenous British breed. In appearance a typical hound, but with a markedly gay look. Tricolour is the usual and most favoured colour. Height and weight vary with the type of country hunted, but 15 in. and 40 lb. may be taken as the maxima.

The Harrier. A larger and rather coarser edition of the Beagle. The height is 18–19 in. and the weight correspondingly heavier than the Beagle.

The Foxhound. A still larger edition of the Beagle. Physically, perhaps, the most perfect animal of its sort in the world. Colour not important: tricolour is common, badger pied less common than a few years ago. Height: 22–24 in. Weight is variable, but usually around 70 lb.

The Welsh Hound. A distinct breed of foxhound. Not recognised by the Kennel Club. Coat: rough, dense and of medium length. The breed is noted for its great powers of scent, great stamina and generous tongue. Colour: black-and-fawn, red, red-and-fawn, tan or tricolour. Height: 23–24 in. Weight: 70–75 lb.

The Basset Hound. First introduced from France in 1866 by Lord Galway. Recognised in 1887. Long-bodied and short-legged. Head remarkably like that of a bloodhound. Coat: smooth. Colour: usual hound colours. Height: 13 in. Weight: 45 lb. Has the most musical voice of any hound.

The Otterhound. Not very uncommon. Only two of the packs of Otterhounds are genuine Otterhounds. The coat should be hard, shaggy but not too long, and there should be a thick woolly undercoat. Colour: grizzle, black, blue, red, usually with tan markings. Height: about 24 in. Weight: about 65 lb.

The Bloodhound. Probably introduced by William the Conqueror. Unmistakable to look at; a very powerful hound with long pendant ears, whose facial expression suggests that he bears the cares of the world. Has remarkable powers of scent. Coat: short, smooth. Colour: black-and-tan, red-and-tan, tawny. Height: 25–27 in. Weight: 90–110 lb.

The Great Dane. This is the old German Boarhound. Beautifully proportioned and remarkably fast for their size, they are not used for sport in this country. The coat is short, dense and smooth. A Great Dane should have a sleek look. Colour: brindle (brindles must be striped, the stripes black and the ground colour yellow or orange), fawn, blue, black and Harlequin (a white ground colour with blue or black patches). Height: 30 in. Weight: dogs 120 lb., bitches 100 lb.

The Dachshund. First introduced in 1860. This is the German badger-hound. It is still used for sport on the Continent, but there is only one pack of working Dachshunds in Britain. There are four distinct types: smooth-haired, long-haired, wire-haired and miniature. Except for the difference in coat, the appearance is the same; very long-bodied and very short-legged. The long-haired should have a soft, slightly wavy coat; the wire-haired's should be short and harsh. The miniature is smooth-haired. In the smooth- and long-haired varieties any colour is allowable except white. All colours are also permissible (except white) in the wire-haired, but iron-grey seems to predominate. The height of standard Dachshunds should be 8–10 in.; that of miniatures 7–8 in. The weight of standard Dachshunds may vary between 12 and 22 lb.; that of the miniature must not exceed 11 lb.

The Dalmatian. There is no official record for the first introduction of this breed. Commonly known as the 'Carriage Dog' or as 'Plum Dough', it has been used for sport (most Dalmatians have excellent noses) and as a pointer, but mainly as a guard for coaches in the hey-day of the coaching era, and to run with carriages in the Victorian era. One may still occasionally see one running between the wheels of a carriage. Coat: short and smooth. Colour: white with black or liver spots. Spots may vary in size from a sixpence to a florin, and should never form patches; the rounder the spots the better. Height: 20–23 in. Weight: dogs 55 lb., bitches 50 lb.

The Rhodesian Ridgeback. First introduced by Mrs. Foljambe in 1928. Very little is known of the history of this manufactured breed. There seems to be little doubt that Great Dane and Bloodhound have contributed largely to its making. The distinctive feature of the breed is a ridge of hair along the back, which grows in the reverse direction to the rest of the coat. The breed is sometimes known as the 'Lion Dog' because it has been used in packs to bay lions. Coat: short and harsh. Colour: dark tan, tawny or brindle. Height: 23–25 in. Weight: 65–70 lb.

THE SHEEPDOG FAMILY

This is one of the three basic families of the domestic dog, the other two being the Spitz and the Greyhound. It is also the family which shows the most variation. One cannot describe a typical sheepdog, since each pastoral country—and that includes most of the countries in the world—has its particular type, which has been evolved to suit particular conditions. Indeed, there are parochial types of sheepdog. But, broadly speaking, sheepdogs can be divided into two main groups—the guards and the herders. In early times, before enclosures became widespread, the principal duty of the sheepdog was to guard the flock against attack from wild beasts. He then walked in front of the flock with the shepherd. Later, when land all over the world began to be fenced, the sheepdog was required to help the shepherd in herding his flock. Guarding now became a matter of secondary importance; what was required was a quick and active dog with plenty of stamina. Thus we find two distinct types: a large, rather heavy type (the old guards), and a smaller, active type, the herders. The former are usually rather short in the back, with roundish heads and fairly short muzzles: the latter are usually rather long in the back, with long muzzles and little or no 'stop'. The true herding sheepdog also has a characteristic loping gait, which enables him to cover a great deal of ground without tiring unduly.

The Border Collie. Not recognised by the Kennel Club. A working dog of a quite distinct and easily recognisable type, but not in any way standardised. Long-bodied and lightly legged, tail long and carried low. The tail is usually white-tipped. Coat: medium in length. Colour: varies a great deal, but the most usual is black with a white blaze and white collar. Height: usually about 18 in. Weight: about 30–35 lb.

The Maltese. One of the oldest known breeds in the world. Until comparatively recently was known as the Maltese Terrier. As the late Arthur Croxton Smith pointed out, it certainly is not a terrier, and the word has now been dropped, though it still occurs in the standard where the head, it is said, 'should be of a Terrier type'. I do not think that anyone who has ever owned one of these quite delightful little dogs, and treated it as a dog and not merely as an ornament, can have any doubt that it is a member of the sheepdog family. It will sit on guard for hours; it will, given the opportunity, herd ducks; and I have even known one attempt to herd cattle in very much the same manner as a Corgi. The head, though of 'terrier shape', should not be narrow or long. The body is short and cobby, set low to the ground, the back level. Coat: of good length, straight and silky. Colour: any self-colour, but preferably pure white. Height: immaterial, but the smaller the better. Weight: not exceeding 10 lb.

The Rough Collie. Originally the show-bench counterpart of the Border Collie, but now a distinct breed and no longer a working dog. Many years of selective breeding have produced a very long muzzle, a flat skull rather narrow between the ears, and a very thick dense coat, harsh to the touch; the undercoat is close, soft and furry. The size has also been greatly increased. As a show dog, the Rough Collie is a singularly handsome animal. Height: 22–24 in. Weight: 55–65 lb.

The Smooth Collie. An uncommon and most attractive variety of the above, differing only in the coat, which is hard, dense and quite smooth.

The Shetland Sheepdog. This very attractive breed has been evolved only within the last sixty years, though small sheepdogs have, of course, been used in Shetland for generations. A miniature Collie in appearance—it comes from the land of miniatures, and must be small since it is required to work with very small sheep—it is light and very agile, and, like all working dogs, very intelligent and full of initiative. In England, the Shetland Sheepdog is purely a show dog or a pet, and a very beautiful one at that. Coat: double, the outer coat long, harsh and straight with mane and frill very abundant and the forelegs well feathered; the undercoat soft, short and close, resembling fur. Colour: tricolour, black-and-white, sable, sable-and-white, blue merle, blue merle-and-white. Height: 14 in. Weight: about 14 lb.

The Old English Sheepdog. This is the type of the 'guard' sheepdog, a short-backed, compact and heavy animal. Though described as 'old', there is no evidence that it has been in England for much more than 250 years. Undoubtedly a descendant of the Russian Owtcharka, the original dogs, as portrayed by eighteenth-century artists, seem to have been a good deal heavier than the modern 'bob-tail'. The lighter weight of the modern dog is no doubt due to the introduction of Bearded Collie blood. The breed is very intelligent and they make excellent guard-dogs. Indeed, if they have a fault, it is that they tend to become a little possessive with increasing age. Despite their weight, they are active and agile, and can clear a five-barred gate without difficulty. But for their coats, which do undoubtedly pick up dirt in bad weather and which are very unsightly when matted, they would, I am sure, be much more popular than they are. Now a show dog only, and a most impressive one. The coat is profuse, shaggy and hard; double coated, the under-coat soft and practically waterproof. The shaggy top coat covers the eyes. Colour: any shade of grey, grizzle, blue or blue merle, with or without white markings. Height: 22–24 in. Weight: about 60 lb.

The Alsatian. Properly called the German Shepherd-dog. First introduced in 1909. Too well known to need description. Among the most intelligent and adaptable of dogs, it has been widely used in war, for police work and as a guide-dog for the blind. It is still worked with sheep on the Continent, and has been worked with them in England. It has also been used as a retriever in the shooting field with success. Coat: double, the topcoat close, hard and flat, the under-coat woolly, dense and practically weatherproof. Colour: all colours are permissible. Height: 22–26 in. Weight: about 60 lb.

The Welsh Corgi (Cardigan). This is undoubtedly the more ancient of the two varieties of Corgi. Easily recognisable by its long tail. The breed is worked regularly with cattle in Wales, and has not become purely a show breed. Coat: short, hard and dense. Tail usually white-tipped. Colour: any colour except pure white. Most dogs have a white blaze and a white collar. Height: 12 in. Weight: 24–26 lb.

The Welsh Corgi (Pembroke). Became immensely popular when taken up by the Royal Family as companions for the young Princesses. Too well known to need description, since it is one of the most popular town dogs of to-day. Coat: smooth and dense, and of medium length. Tail docked. Colour: red, sable, fawn, black-and-tan. White marking on head, legs, chest and neck is usual. Height: 10–12 in. Weight: 18–24 lb.

THE MASTIFF FAMILY

One of the most ancient of the families of the domestic dog. The distinguishing characteristic is the heavy build and large square head with a short, square muzzle and a marked 'stop'. In this family there are to be found most of the largest dogs in the world.

The Mastiff. This ancient breed, which has always been closely associated with Britain, almost died out during the war. I believe I am correct in saying that only three litters were born in Britain during the war, and that only one puppy survived the war. At the end of the war there were probably not more than a score of mastiffs in the country, and most of these were more than eight years old. New blood (though, in fact, it was good English blood) was imported from America, and the breed is now gradually increasing in numbers, and is certainly firmly re-established. But it is too large ever to become common in modern Britain. The coat is short and close-lying, the ears small, thin and pendant. The muzzle is short, broad under the eyes. The 'stop' is very definite. Colour: apricot, silver, fawn, fawn-brindle. Muzzle, ears and nose black. Height: 30 in. Weight: 165 lb.

The Bull Mastiff. A new breed, evolved in Britain barely forty years ago and granted recognition in 1927. Bred from bulldog and mastiff, a cross in which mastiff blood predominated. They make excellent guard- and police-dogs, and are much used in this type of work. In appearance similar to the mastiff, but smaller and squarer, giving the impression of enormous power. Coat: short, hard and flat. Colour: any shade of brindle, fawn or red. Mask black. Height: 24–27 in. Weight: dogs 110–130 lb., bitches 90–110 lb.

The Bulldog. Popularly accepted as the British national dog, and commonly considered one of our most ancient breeds. In its present form, however, it is quite modern. The skull should be very large—in circumference (round in front of the ears) at least the height of the dog at the shoulders—and the 'stop' pronounced. The jaw should be broad and square, and markedly undershot; the chest very wide and deep; the back short, strong and roached; the belly tucked up. Coat: fine, short and close. Colour: any whole colour, except black or black-and-tan, which are considered undesirable. Height: about 16 in. Weight: dogs 55 lb., bitches 50 lb.

The French Bulldog. Not a miniature Bulldog, but a distinct breed and quite different in appearance. Head massive, square and broad. Ears upright and 'bat-like' in contrast to British Bulldog's 'rose' ear. Short, cobby, muscular body, well developed at shoulders and narrowing to loins. The teeth should not be visible when the mouth is closed. Coat: fine, smooth and close. Colour: dark brindle and pied are preferred. Height: about 12 in. Weight: dogs 28 lb., bitches 24 lb.

The Boxer. Though first introduced by Mrs. Sprigge in 1933—it is possible that there may have been one or two in England before that —there is something to be said for the Boxer enthusiasts' contention that this is a British breed reintroduced. There is undoubtedly some of the old British Bulldog blood in it. The head is broad with the top of the skull slightly arched, and the forehead shows a distinct 'stop'. The head should not show deep wrinkles. The muzzle square with strong jaws and slightly undershot. There must never be the exaggerated appearance of the Bulldog. The back should be straight, broad and very musclar. Tail docked, carried upwards. Coat: smooth, short and tight to the body. Colour: brindle, fawn or red. Brindles should have black stripes on a golden-yellow or reddish background. White markings are not considered undesirable. Height: variable, but between 21–24 in. Weight: depends upon height. A 23-in. dog should weigh about 66 lb., a 22-in. bitch about 62 lb.

The Boston Terrier. One of the very few truly American breeds. Was evolved about 1870 from the French Bulldog and the old English Bull Terrier (the Staffordshire fighting terrier), with perhaps a little of the old English Bulldog thrown in. French Bulldog blood predominates. Introduced in 1927. Head short and square, and flat on top; free from wrinkles. The muzzle short, square, wide and deep; jaw powerful and slightly undershot. The ears are erect and 'bat-like', but not so large as in the French Bulldog. Body short but not chunky. Coat: short, smooth and fine, with a good gloss. Colour: brindle with white markings; rich black with clean white blaze is a common colour and very striking. Weight: ranges between 15 and 25 lb.

The Newfoundland. Though known in Newfoundland at least 200 years ago as a draught dog, was not exhibited in England until 1864. Has never gained great popularity here. Not strictly an American breed; originally a central European breed which has been re-imported. A massive animal with a flat, dense and rather coarse coat. The colour should be a dull jet-black, though black-and-white and black-and-bronze examples do occur. Height: 26–28 in. Weight: 120–150 lb.

The St. Bernard. A breed whose history has been completely submerged in legend and myth, but closely related to the Newfoundland. First introduced about 1840. A large and massive animal with a broad skull, slightly rounded on top and a well-defined stop. A broad, straight back and a wide and deep chest. The legs should be heavily boned. Coat: dense and flat with well-feathered thighs. Colour: orange, mahogany-brindle, red-brindle, white with patches of any of these colours. Height: about 28 in. Weight: about 200 lb. There is also a smooth variety, which differs only in the close, hound-like coat.

The Pyrenean Mountain Dog. A close relative of the St. Bernard and Newfoundland. First introduced by Lady Sybil Grant in 1911. The breed died out during the First World War and was reintroduced in 1934. One of the most magnificent of all domestic dogs, with a temperament to match its beauty. Of great size, with a large, rather bear-like head. Coat: long, flat and thick with an under-coat which is fine and dense. Colour: white, or white with lemon, biscuit, tan or badger-grey markings. Height: 27–32 in. Weight: dogs about 125 lb., bitches about 115 lb.

The Pug. Introduced into England before the seventeenth century. In all respects, save for the curled tail, a miniature mastiff, with the mastiff's massive head, fine short coat and very strong legs. Colour: silver, fawn or black. Height: about 11 in. Weight: 14–18 lb.

The Chihuahua. Hubbard places this breed in the Spaniel family. I include it with the Mastiffs, on historical grounds and not because it resembles the rest of the family (though the ears bear some resemblance to those of the French Bulldog and the Boston Terrier). The breed was in Mexico when the Spaniards first reached that country, being kept both as a pet and for food. The Spaniards eat many of them. From their descriptions there can be little doubt that at that time they resembled Pugs much more closely than they do now. Centuries of selective breeding, and perhaps a cross of Papillon blood during the Spanish occupation, has altered their appearance, but the character is still much more that of the mastiff than of the spaniel. Coat: short, fine and glossy. Colour: immaterial, but the most common colour is white with tan, blue or black markings. Height: 6–9 in. Weight: 4–6 lb. The smallest of all domestic dogs, one has been recorded weighing only 1¾ lb.

THE SPANIEL FAMILY

Originally an off-shoot of the sheepdog family. The family is, in general, distinguished by the broad skull, domed across the top, long, pendant ears and full round eyes.

The Papillon. I place this breed first in the family, because it is not typical and because it follows naturally upon the Chihuahua. Indeed, there are those who believe that the Papillon is descended from the Chihuahua. I do not, however, believe that the latter was brought from Mexico by the Spaniards (there would surely have been some record had that been the case, for the Spaniards have always been very dog-conscious), though I think it very probable that the Spaniards took the Papillon to Mexico. Certainly, the breed has a very long history in Europe, especially Mediterranean Europe, though it was not introduced to England until 1923. In the variety best known in this country the ears are large and erect and heavily fringed. But for the fringe, they might well be the ears of the Chihuahua. The drop-eared variety, which is undoubtedly the older, is not so well known in England. This variety is a typical small spaniel. The head is small, slightly domed between the ears, with a pointed muzzle of medium length. (The muzzle is more pointed now than it was when the breed was introduced.) The tail is long and heavily fringed, and carried in a curl, falling over the back. Coat: long, fine and silky. Colour: white with black or coloured patches, or tricolour. Height: a maximum of 12 in. Weight: a maximum of 12 lb. There are many small show specimens—6 lb. being considered the ideal weight—but the usual household dog weighs about 10 lb.

The Pekingese. First definitely mentioned in Chinese literature in A.D. 618. First introduced into Britain in 1860, but was undoubtedly known in Europe long before that date, and perhaps in Venice in the fifteenth century. Too well known to require any description. Coat: long and straight, with a profuse mane forming a frill round the neck and extending behind the shoulders. Colours: all colours are permissible, except liver. Size is very variable, but 12 lb. should be considered the maximum weight. Many dogs—sometimes known as 'Sleeve Dogs'—weigh only 6 or 7 lb.

The Japanese Spaniel. Another very ancient breed. Indeed, it has been suggested that the Pekingese, mentioned in A.D. 618 as coming from Fu-lin, may have come from Japan. It is more generally accepted that the Pekingese was introduced into Japan about A.D. 670. Since no one now knows where Fu-lin was (except that it was definitely not a part of China)—the concluding part of the passage referred to runs 'and then it was for the first time that there were dogs of Fu-lin

Bedlington (Old type: illustration by Arthur Wardle).

Bedlington.

Sealyham.

Scottish Terrier.

in China'—there can be no certainty on the point. First introduced about 1850. The breed bears a strong resemblance to the Pekingese, but stands higher on the leg and is rather lighter in build, with straight legs and fine bones. The head is rather large for the size of the dog. The ideal body should be squarely built, and in length about the same as the height of the dog. Coat: long, straight and profuse, abundantly feathered on the thighs and tail. Colour: either black-and-white or red-and-white. (The term red includes lemon, sable and orange.) Height: up to 10 in. Weight: 6–9 lb.

THE SETTERS

'Stonehenge' expressed the opinion that Setters were the outcome of a cross betwen Pointer and Spaniel. Pointers and Spaniels were crossed from time to time in the nineteenth century—the cross was known as a 'dropper'—but such a cross had nothing to do with the formation of the Setter, which is the original 'setting spaniel', and was known to Gervase Markham under the name 'Setting-dogge' in the middle of the seventeenth century. Setters are long-legged, rather 'rangy' dogs, lithe and muscular, designed to cover a lot of country in a day.

The English Setter. Perhaps the original setting spaniel from Spain. Gervase Markham's description suggests that the dogs of his day resembled the modern English Setter in many ways, and even in colour. But the breed was not established as a distinct breed until the early nineteenth century, when Edward Laverack, who started his work in 1825, perfected the type. Laverack's mantle fell on Purcell Llewellin, who bred some really beautiful dogs. The English Setter is now rarely seen in the shooting field (though a good working dog), and is far from common on the show-bench. The head is long and lean with a well-defined stop, and oval between the ears. The ears are of moderate length and hang close to the cheek. The neck is long and muscular, and the shoulders are well set back. The forearm is very muscular, and the pasterns short, muscular and straight. The feet (very important in a gundog) are compact and well-protected with hair between the toes. Coat: silky and of moderate length, well feathered on the legs and the tail flagged. Height: 24–27 in. Weight: 56–66 lb.

The Gordon Setter. This is the old black-and-tan setter, first mentioned by Gervase Markham in 1665. It was improved by the Duke of

Richmond and Gordon about 1820, who is said to have used some working collie blood. Later still, some bloodhound blood is said to have been introduced. One still comes across a bloodhound type with heavy head and ears from time to time, and also a collie type with pointed muzzle occasionally. Both are regarded with extreme disfavour by specialists. The ideal head should be deep rather than broad, with a well-defined stop and nicely rounded between the ears. The body is the typical setter body, but has the appearance of being rather more heavily built than the English Setter. Coat: soft and fine with little or no wave, the legs feathered and the tail flagged. Colour: coal-black with tan markings. Height: 26 in. Weight: about 65 lb.

The Irish Setter. Little or nothing is known of the origin of the Irish Setter. It is not mentioned before 1803, but was then evidently already established as a distinct breed in Ireland. It did not become at all popular in England until about 1880, having acquired a reputation for 'unsteadiness' in the shooting field. It has now almost disappeared from the English shooting scene (though still worked in Ireland), but has become immensely popular on the show-bench both here and in America. It is, indeed, easily the best known of the group. A typical Setter in body, it is lighter and more rangy in build than the English Setter, and has a much more racy appearance. Coat: flat and soft, and of moderate length, with little or no wave. Colour: rich chestnut. Height: 26 in. Weight: 60 lb.

The Pointer. The Pointer is the direct descendant of the Perdiguero, the partridge dog, mentioned by Cervantes in *Don Quixote*. There can be no doubt that the breed came from Spain, but at what date is uncertain. The first record we have is a picture of the Duke of Kingston, dated 1725, in which he is shown with his pointers. These dogs are finer in shape than the rather heavy dogs of Spain, which indicates that they had already been in this country for some time, and had perhaps been crossed with French pointer blood, for the French had also fined down the Spanish Perdiguero. The modern English Pointer looks very much like a smooth-coated Setter in general appearance. Coat: fine, smooth, hard and with a definite sheen. Colour: lemon-and-white, orange-and-white, liver-and-white, black-and-white, whole colours or tricolour. Height: 24–25 in. Weight: 50–55 lb.

The Dobermann Pinscher. A German pointer breed evolved about 1890 by Herr Dobermann in Thuringia, using Pinscher, Weimeraner and Vorstehund blood lines. The breed, which is noted for its intelligence, is well known on the Continent, particularly in France and Holland, and is very popular in the United States, where it is much used for police work. It is gaining in popularity in this country, and is now used by a number of county constabularies. The head is long and clean cut, with a slight stop and a powerful muzzle. The body is powerful, the back short and level, and the chest deep. The legs are long and the feet small and compact. The tail is docked very short. The dog gives the appearance of great power and stamina. Coat: short and harsh. Colour: black, tan and blue with red markings. Height: about 25 in. Weight: 45–50 lb.

The German Short-haired Pointer. A new breed to Britain. This is, in fact, the Vorstehund, which is the most popular and widely used of the German pointers, and has long been popular in other European countries. Why, since we use other German names, such as the Dachshund and the Schnauzer, without difficulty, we should refuse to use Vorstehund and prefer the cumbersome English name is impossible to understand. There was some prejudice against the breed to begin with on the grounds that pointers should not be docked, but interest is now increasing steadily. There is little chance of their becoming popular in the shooting field (though they are, in fact, superb gundogs), but they have been adopted for police work, for which their intelligence, powerful build and great scenting powers make them most suitable. They are very popular in the United States. Coat: short, hard and tough, over a loose skin. Tail docked short. Colour: chestnut, chestnut-and-white, roan. Height: about 26 in. Weight: about 60 lb.

THE RETRIEVERS

Dogs have, of course, been trained to retrieve from the earliest times. It is an act which seems to come naturally to every puppy, no matter what the breed, in the normal course of play. Certainly, the earlier sportsmen trained setters and pointers to retrieve. Gervase Markham, in fact, gives instructions in the art of training to retrieve. But the retriever proper—that is the dog used for the sole purpose of retrieving game, a dog with a good nose and little or no disposition to hunt—is a modern creation, not more than a century old. The retrievers spring from the setters—in many the family likeness is unmistakable—but other blood was also used. What this was is not known for certain. General Hutchinson [1] was of the opinion that Newfoundland blood played a not unimportant part, and it may be that some bloodhound blood and some foxhound blood was also introduced. While, personally, I am very doubtful about the Newfoundland blood, I think that a slight strain of hound blood, introduced about 1850 to increase 'nose', is probable.

The Flat-coated Retriever. Developed in the latter half of the nineteenth century, possibly from the Gordon Setter and the Labrador. Originally known as the 'wavy-coat', the Flat-coated Retriever held undisputed sway, both in the shooting field and on the show-bench, until the early years of this century. This was very largely due to the skilful breeding policy of S. E. Shirley, the founder of the Kennel Club, and later to that of H. Reginald Cooke, one of whose dogs won at field trials in 1949, when his owner was aged 91. To-day the breed is rarely seen in the field (having been ousted by the Labrador) and is far from plentiful on the show-bench. A good Flat-coat is an active, powerful dog, with a long, nicely shaped head, the skull flat and moderately broad and with but a slight stop. The chest is deep and fairly broad, the back short and square and well ribbed-up, and the quarters very muscular. Coat: dense and of fine texture, and as flat as possible. Colour: black or liver. Height: about 23 in. Weight: 60–70 lb.

The Curly-coated Retriever. The oldest of the genuine retriever breeds. 'Stonehenge', writing in 1859, maintained that it was a cross between the Newfoundland and the Irish Water Spaniel. By Newfoundland he meant what is now known as the Labrador. Others have contended that Poodle blood was used with the Irish Water Spaniel, which, in my opinion, is much more probable. To-day the breed is rare both in the shooting field and on the show-bench. A curly coat is difficult to keep in good order, but this is such a remarkably beautiful breed that its rarity on the show-bench is little short of astonishing. As a working dog the breed was almost ideal and was held in high favour by gamekeepers, but has now suffered the same fate as the Flat-coat at the hands of the Labrador. The coat should be one mass of short crisp curls from the occiput bone

[1] *Dog Breaking,* 1847.

to the point of the tail. Colour : black or liver. Height : about 26 in. Weight : 70–80 lb.

The Labrador Retriever. It is commonly believed—one finds the statement repeated in book after book—that the Labrador Retriever came originally in fishing-boats calling at Poole, Dorset. I have seen it stated that the Labrador is indigenous to Labrador, and the same book gives the date for the original landing as 1793. The date most usually given is 1835. Most of this is legend. Labrador at that time was practically uninhabited, and one has only to consider the Labrador in relation to the dogs of the Arctic Circle and its fringe to realise that it is certainly not indigenous. In any case, the name was not used until 1878. 'Stonehenge' and others of his period always speak of the St. John's Newfoundland, and evidently mean a dog smaller than the Newfoundland proper. Dogs of this sort were certainly kept by the Earl of Malmesbury about 1835, and there does seem to be some truth in the story that he got the first one, at least, from a fishing-boat in Poole Harbour. Later he got some more and built up a kennel, but he called these dogs Newfoundlands until 1876. In 1878, however, he called a bitch, Juno, a Labrador. It is reasonable to suppose, therefore, that he detected some difference between this animal and his Newfoundlands. In any case, it was Labradors that he gave to the Duke of Buccleuch in 1882. There is a two-year gap here—from Lord Malmesbury's Sweep, a Newfoundland, of 1876 to his Juno, a Labrador, of 1878—which cannot now be filled. It is worth while pointing out once more that the word 'Labrador' is Spanish, and that Velazquez was painting animals reasonably like the modern Labrador and, moreover, in a sporting context. The breed did not begin to gain wide popularity until 1903, since when it has pretty well swept the board of other retrievers. The modern Labrador is too well known to require description. It is a strongly built, short-coupled, very active dog, rather wider in the head and chest than other retrievers. Coat: short and dense, with a weather-resisting undercoat. Colour : black or yellow. Height : about 22 in. Weight : about 65 lb.

(The Yellow Labrador Retriever is sometimes regarded as a distinct breed, and some authorities maintain that the yellow colour is a sign of Chesapeake Bay blood. The fact is that yellow puppies occur in the litters of black parents quite frequently—the breed carries a gene for yellow. The first Yellow Labrador to become a

Dual Champion (Mr. Winter's 'Staindrop Saighdear' in 1947) was the son of black parents. The Dual Champion of 1949 was also a Yellow Labrador (Mrs. Wormald's 'Knaith Banjo') and he also was the son of black parents.)

The Golden Retriever. This is another breed whose early history has been clouded by legend. The story—commonly repeated in book after book and widely believed—is that the breed owes its origin to a troupe of performing dogs. It is said that the Hon. Dudley Marjoribanks (later Lord Tweedmouth) saw these dogs in a circus at Brighton shortly after the Crimean War, and was so impressed by their cleverness that he bought the whole troupe, sent them to his estate in Scotland, and had them trained to the gun. The troupe is said to have come from Russia, which is, I suppose, the origin of the belief, fostered by some authorities, that the Golden Retriever is a direct descendant of the Caucasian Sheepdog. It is a pleasant story—though it reveals a remarkable ignorance of the circus and circus tradition—and it was given currency, in perfectly good faith, by the late Arthur Croxton Smith. There is not a word of truth in it, as Croxton Smith himself was careful to point out at a later date. However, the romantic story was, by then, too firmly entrenched, and I suppose that no amount of denial will now serve to kill it completely. The true facts are these: the Hon. Edward Marjoribanks saw a very good-looking yellow retriever at Brighton in the late sixties, and managed to buy it from its owner, a cobbler, who had been given the dog, in payment of a debt, by a keeper in the neighbourhood. The dog had been the one yellow puppy in a litter of black wavy-coated retrievers. Later, Lord Tweedmouth found another yellow dog, a bitch, also the puppy of black parents. He bred from these two. To avoid continual inbreeding he crossed with black wavy-coated retriever bitches. The litters always contained a proportion of yellow puppies, and so the breed was established. The story that a bloodhound cross was used at one time is also quite untrue, as is the tale that this cross proved so disastrous that Irish Setter blood was used to restore the balance. The Golden Retriever is a pure-bred retriever, an offshoot from the black Flat-coated Retriever. The head is broad with a wide and powerful muzzle and a well-defined stop, and the short-coupled body is well-balanced, strong and deep through the heart. Coat: flat or wavy, with good feathering and a dense undercoat. Colour: any shade of gold or cream, but not red or mahogany. There is, in fact, a good deal of variation in colour. Height: about 23 in. Weight: dogs 65–75 lb., bitches 55–60 lb.

THE SPANIELS

The Spaniels proper have been evolved from the Setters within comparatively recent times, certainly within the last two hundred years. Early sporting literature is full of references to Spaniels, but the references are always to Setting Spaniels. No distinction was made in those days between Setters and Spaniels, for the simple reason that there was no distinction to be made. The only possible distinction that could be made was between land Spaniels and Water Spaniels; a distinction which holds good to-day. Furthermore, it was not until the opening years of this century that it was possible to make any real distinction—with the exception of the Irish Water Spaniel and the Clumber Spaniel—between the breeds. Even as late as 1900 it was possible, and indeed quite common, to have three varieties in a single litter. In such a case, the taller dogs were called Springers, the shorter Cockers, and any that were liver-coloured were termed Sussex. Now, of course, the differences between the breeds are sharply accentuated, and no one has the least difficulty in recognising at least the common varieties.

The Poodle. It is very difficult nowadays to persuade people that the Poodle is not merely an exotic pet for ladies or men of unusual tastes; difficult, indeed, to persuade some people that it is not merely a joke. Undoubtedly many Poodles are made to look eccentric by the manner in which they are trimmed, and by the fact that many women, not content with a fantastic trim, will persist in decking them out with bows of coloured ribbon. In fact, the Poodle, a dog of quite remarkable intelligence (as is shown by its popularity and success in the circus ring), is, when treated properly, an excellent working dog. It is commonplace nowadays to speak of the 'French Poodle', but the name actually comes from the German *pudeln*, meaning 'to splash in water'. And here we have the origin of the dog: it is a water spaniel. Though France, Germany and Russia have been given as the original home of the breed by various authorities, there can, I think, be no doubt whatever that it is the direct descendant of the Cao d'Agua, the Portuguese Water-dog. Indeed, I have seen working examples of the Cao d'Agua in Portuguese fishing villages which might easily have been mistaken for large Poodles. These Portuguese Water-dogs are clipped from the ribs to the stern; not from fashion, but to facilitate movement in the water. Poodles used for sport—and they are still widely used in France and are occasionally used in England—were clipped for the same reason. It is unfortunate that fashion should have brought a fine dog to ridicule. The breed is too well known to warrant description : a good Poodle should be a very active, intelligent, well-built dog with a good action, and should carry himself proudly. Coat: very profuse and of a good hard texture. Colour: all black, all white, all brown, all blue. Height : 15 in. plus. Weight: 20–30 lb.

(The Miniature Poodle, which should stand less than 15 in., should be in every respect a miniature of the Standard Poodle. The Miniature is a twentieth-century revival of a type that was extremely popular in the eighteenth century, especially in Spain. It is, unfortunately, true that the breeding of the Miniature in recent years has not always been as careful as one could wish, and one does see—though not at the shows—some very distressing examples being dragged about the streets.)

The Irish Water Spaniel. It is sometimes said by enthusiastic Irishmen that the Irish Water Spaniel has been in Ireland since pre-Christian times. Let it be said at once that there is no proof whatsoever to support this contention. The breed is, obviously, another descendant of the Cao d'Agua, and it is very probable, having regard to the long and close connection between Ireland and the Iberian Peninsula, that it has been established in Ireland for centuries. But its known history does not begin before the nineteenth century. Mr. Justin McCarthy began breeding in 1828, and it is to Mr. Justin McCarthy that the Irish Water Spaniel owes its fame. In recent years the most famous breeder has been Mr. F. Trench O'Rorke, who about 1923 began breeding some beautiful dogs and gaining great success both at the shows and in trials. But, despite the fact that the Irish Water Spaniel is one of the best all-round gundogs and beyond compare in the water, it has never become really popular in England. In America, on the other hand, it is highly esteemed and widely employed, particularly in the Southern States. In England, the Irish Water Spaniel is never clipped in the manner of the Cao d'Agua. I have, however, seen one or two clipped dogs at work in Ireland. Clipping would not be countenanced for show, of course. The Irish Water Spaniel is a smart, upstanding, strongly built dog with a gait quite unlike that of a land spaniel, but not unlike that of a poodle. The head is well domed, and the muzzle long, strong, rather square, with a moderate stop. The feet are large, round and spreading, and well covered with hair over and between the toes. Coat: a mass of close, dense ringlets, the hair having a natural oiliness. The tail is short and thick at the root, tapering to a fine point. Three or four inches at the root are covered with close curls, the rest bare. Colour: rich dark liver with a purplish tint (puce-liver). Height: about 23 in. Weight: 60–65 lb.

The Clumber Spaniel. This is the oldest of the British breeds of land spaniel used for sport. It is also the largest of the British spaniels, and so unlike the others in appearance that it is evident that it has not been evolved from the setting spaniels in the normal way. Tradition says that the Duc de Noailles presented four to the second Duke of Newcastle about 1770. In this case, tradition probably speaks truth. At least there is a picture, painted by Francis Wheatley, R.A., in 1788, which shows the second Duke on his shooting pony, accompanied by four unquestionable Clumbers. The breed, in fact, is French in origin. Beyond that one cannot go. There is a suggestion that it may be derived from the Alpine Spaniel. There is also a suggestion that Basset Hound blood was introduced early in the eighteenth century. The modern Clumber is probably a good deal heavier than his ancestors, and this makes them slow in the field in comparison with other land spaniels. Perhaps this is the reason why they have never been popular in the shooting field (though they have always had a small body of most enthusiastic supporters), and to-day it is very rare indeed to see one at work. It is a pity because, as workers, especially when used in teams, they have no equal among the spaniels. However, the days when a man might work a team of spaniels at a shoot have gone for ever. Unfortunately, too, fewer are now to be seen on the show-bench. The Clumber has a large head, square and massive; the nose square and flesh-coloured. The neck is fairly long, thick and powerful, and the body long and heavy, with a broad straight back and very powerful hindquarters. Coat: abundant, close, silky and straight, with the legs well feathered. Colour: white with lemon markings. Orange markings occur but are not liked. Height: about 18 in. Weight: dogs about 70 lb., bitches about 60 lb.

The Cocker Spaniel. A fairly small setting spaniel existed in England in the seventeenth century. A portrait by Van Dyck of the Prince and Princess of Wales shows two of these dogs, long-backed but definitely shorter in the leg than the usual setting spaniel of the time. There can be no doubt, I think, that it was from dogs of this type that the Cocker Spaniel was developed. But the name 'cocking spaniel' did not come into use until the late eighteenth century, when these dogs were used particularly for flushing woodcock. The breed as we know it to-day may be said to date from 1870, when James Farrow began to breed them to a particular mould. The name Cocker Spaniel was officially recognised in 1892. It is now one of the most popular of all breeds (it is usual for Cocker entries at the shows to exceed those of any other breed) and is far too well known to require description. This great popularity as a show dog has inevitably resulted in a decline in popularity as a working dog, since some of the points particularly admired on the show-bench are just those which militate against good work in thick cover. Coat: flat, close and silky in texture. Colour: various colours, but in self-colours there should be no white except on the chest. Height: about 16 in. Weight: 25–28 lb.

The English Springer Spaniel. A type of setting spaniel originally trained for springing game for greyhounds, falconry or the net. During the nineteenth century there were a number of different strains, each with a considerable local reputation, the best known of which were the Norfolk and the Boughey, named respectively after a Duke of Norfolk and the Boughey family of Shropshire. But there was no definite type. Type did not begin to be defined until about 1902. The English Springer Spaniel, the longest on the leg of the modern British land spaniels and much stronger than the Cocker, makes an excellent all-round dog for the shooting-man and is becoming increasingly popular in the field. Coat: soft, close, straight and weather resisting. Colour: black-and-white, liver-and-white, lemon-and-white or tricolour, but any land spaniel colour is accepted for show. Height: about 20 in. Weight: about 50 lb.

The Welsh Springer Spaniel. Possibly a descendant of the red-and-white setting spaniel which was common in England in the eighteenth century. A smaller edition of the English Springer and easily distinguished from its cousin, not only by the smaller size but also because the ears are not so large nor so well feathered. Another excellent all-round gun-dog, active and strong. Colour: dark red and white only. Height: about 17 in. Weight: 35–45 lb.

The Sussex Spaniel. Originally developed to suit the special conditions of the county from which it takes its name, heavy soil, thick hedgerows and big woods with thick undergrowth: conditions which demanded a very powerful, short-legged dog. Sussex spaniels, strong liver-coloured dogs, were known as Relf Spaniels at the end of the eighteenth century, the name being derived from Albert Relf, the head keeper on Mr. Fuller's estate near Hastings, who developed the type, though the credit is usually given to his employer. The Sussex Spaniel is the only spaniel to 'speak' at his work. The strong bell-like babble is not liked by Field Trial judges as a whole, but is undoubtedly valuable in the sort of country in which the dog has to work. The breed is now uncommon, but seems to be recovering a little of the popularity it had before the First World War. Coat: flat and abundant. Colour: rich golden liver. Height: 15–16 in. Weight: 40–50 lb.

The Field Spaniel. Originally, the Field Spaniel was developed to provide a spaniel heavier than the Cocker to meet special conditions. What was wanted was a dog with shorter legs than the Cocker, heavier bone, and a more compact, more powerful body. Cocker and Sussex blood was used, and the type was fixed by 1870. It seems to have been moderately popular in the shooting field until about the end of the century, but was then ruined by exhibitors, who shortened the legs and lengthened the bodies so much that the unfortunate dogs became known as 'caterpillars' and were rendered quite unfit for work. Sanity returned after the First World War, and the modern Field Spaniel is a handsome dog and, as its occasional appearances at trials prove, quite a good worker. It would be an exaggeration, however, to say that the breed has much support. Coat: flat or slightly waved, silky in texture, dense. Colour: should be a self-coloured dog or self-coloured with tan. Height: about 18 in. Weight: about 40 lb.

The King Charles Spaniel. Popularly described as the oldest English 'toy' breed, the King Charles Spaniel is certainly not English in origin. The probable country of origin is Spain, but 'toy' spaniels were known in Venice in the fifteenth century, and it may be that by that time the Spanish dogs had already received an infusion of Pekingese blood. Toy spaniels—the Spaniel Gentle or Comforter—were known in Britain in the sixteenth century, and a few had probably been in the country since the fourteenth. Until comparatively recently, four varieties were recognised: the King Charles (black-and-tan), the Tricolour, the Blenheim (red-and-white) and the Ruby. Colour distinctions have been abolished—though the varieties still exist—since 1920, all being grouped under the name of King Charles Spaniels. Coat: long, silky and straight, a slight wave is allowable but no curl. Legs, ears and tail profusely feathered. Colour: the four varieties mentioned above. 'Ruby' is a whole rich chestnut red. Height: about 10 in. Weight: 6–12 lb.

The Cavalier King Charles Spaniel. A new breed, based on the toy spaniel of King Charles II's reign. The breed owes it existence to Mr. Roswell Eldridge of New York, who at Cruft's Show in 1926 offered two prizes of £25 each for dogs of the old-fashioned type. He was moved to do this—and to continue the prizes for the next five years—because breeders of the King Charles had gone so far in distortion that they had produced an abnormally short face with the nose pushed back between the eyes, and it was even hinted that pug blood had been used to produce this 'ideal'. The Kennel Club recognised the new breed in 1944, and it has grown steadily in popularity ever since. Registrations since 1949 have consistently outnumbered those for King Charles Spaniels. Though described as a 'toy', the Cavalier King Charles often approaches the Cocker in size. The head should be almost flat between the ears and the stop shallow. Coat: long and silky, free from curl, but with plenty of feather. Colour: black-and-tan, tricolour, Blenheim (rich chestnut markings on a pearly white ground) and ruby. Black-and-white also occurs, but is not regarded as desirable by exhibitors. Height: about 12 in. Weight: 10–18 lb.

THE TERRIER FAMILY

Originally 'terrier' was the name applied to dogs which were trained to the earths of foxes or the settes of badgers. These were dogs built low to the ground and noted for their courage. The name soon came to be applied to any dog used for the destruction of vermin. The family is, in general, distinguished by its small to medium size, its robust, close-knit, well-muscled body and the rather long head with small triangular ears. The majority of the family have short, rough coats, with a dense soft undercoat. Terriers, as a whole, are amongst the hardiest of all dogs. Another family characteristic is eagerness: they are most alert and active. This eagerness can, in the household dog, become—and often does become—a noisy excitability, if it is not suitably checked in puppyhood. To-day, terriers are to be found everywhere, in town and country alike, and, though many are still used for vermin destruction and many more still show an interest in rat-runs and rat-holes, many more have become household pets pure and simple, and seem to have lost the natural instincts of the family altogether. At one time it would be true to say that almost every district had its own type of terrier—there were, for example, no fewer than eight types in the Lake District alone—and it is only comparatively recently that this multitude of types has become standardised into the breeds now recognised. All the same, there are still numbers of terriers about the country which do not fit into any of the recognised breeds precisely, but which do not deserve to be dismissed (as they usually are) as mongrels.

The Airedale Terrier. The largest of the British terriers. The breed was manufactured about 1850 from a number of local types of terrier with a cross of either Otterhound or Welsh Hound. Most authorities seem to favour an Otterhound cross, but, personally, I think that the late Mr. Holland Buckley, the father of the present secretary of the Kennel Club, who was a great Airedale authority and the founder of the specialist club, was right in maintaining that it was the Welsh Hound. The breed was officially recognised in 1884. Less excitable than the majority of terriers, the Airedale was much used for police work before the coming of the Alsatian. The head is long and flat on top with little or no stop, and the muzzle long and powerful. The back is short, straight, level and strong, and the chest deep but not broad. Coat: short, hard, dense and wiry. Colour: black or dark grizzle, tan markings on each side of the head and the legs tan up to the thighs and elbows. Height: about 24 in. Weight: about 48 lb.

The Australian Terrier. This breed was manufactured in Australia about 1880, and has been exhibited there since at least the late nineties. A large number of breeds have been credited in helping in its formation, among them the Skye, the Paisley, the Dandie Dinmont and the Glen of Imaal. I should, personally, have thought that Cairn and Yorkshire blood had played a bigger part than any of those mentioned above, though possibly introduced at a later date. The modern Australian Terrier, which was introduced to England about 1908, has very much the appearance of the Norwich Terrier. It is an excellent, lively, sporting little dog and a fine ratter, which has not been spoilt by the show-bench. Coat: straight, some 2 in. long, and hard. Tail docked. Colour: blue or silver grey body with tan on legs and face, sandy or red. Height: about 10 in. Weight: about 11 lb.

The Bedlington Terrier. Named from the village of Bedlington in Northumberland, it was originally known as the Rothbury Terrier after the gypsies of Rothbury Forest, who bred it very carefully (as they do Lurchers to-day). A dog of this breed, named 'Peachem', was famous with the local hunts around 1750. Another, named 'Old Flint', was yet more famous in 1782. These dogs were straight backed, fairly low to the ground, very fast and very strong. A whippet cross seems to have been introduced about 1879. The modern Bedlington is quite unlike any other terrier. Coat: thick and linty, twisty but not wiry. Colour: blue, blue-and-tan, liver, sandy. Height: about 16 in. Weight: 18–23 lb.

The Black-and-tan Miniature Terrier. This is the breed that used to be known as the Toy Manchester Terrier. The true miniature seems to have appeared about 1850—there is no certainty on the point—and these little dogs, though they weighed no more than 6 lb. were perfectly capable of killing rats. About 1880 they were taken up by the show fancy, with the result that the weight was reduced to 2–4 lb. and most of the soundness lost. There has been a great improvement in recent years, though many of the modern dogs are still too light in bone. Those that do meet the show standard exactly are quite charming, and certainly not lacking in courage. Coat: smooth, close, short and glossy. Colour: black-and-tan. Height: about 9 in. Weight: not to exceed 8 lb.

The Border Terrier. This is an example of a breed standardised in this century from a number of local and ancient types common along the English-Scottish border. The name is actually derived from the Border Foxhounds, who used small red terriers. The breed is still used for fox, otter and badger, and is famed for its courage. It is frequently stated that no terrier could kill a badger single-handed

—and, indeed, this is a feat beyond the capacity of most dogs—but a Border Terrier, named 'Titlington Peter', belonging to the Percy Hunt, did kill a full-grown badger single-handed in the late twenties. Despite its great courage and great fondness for sport, the Border Terrier makes a good household pet, being exceptionally gentle with children, and developing, in my experience, a fondness for cats. The head is unlike that of most terriers, resembling an otter's. The tail is not docked. Coat: harsh and dense, with a close undercoat. Colour: red, wheaten, grizzle-and-tan, blue-and-tan. Height: about 12 in. Weight: 13–15½ lb.

The Bull Terrier. Originally a Bulldog and Terrier cross, produced for baiting sports. The Bulldog used was, of course, nothing like the modern Bulldog, but more nearly resembled the modern Staffordshire Bull Terrier. The advent of dog shows brought about a change in the Bull Terrier, due mainly to the work of Mr. James Hinks, who produced a white Bull Terrier with a much longer head and a more shapely body. Good examples of the modern Bull Terrier (there are, unfortunately, many bad ones who are too long and weak in the back) are grand, powerful dogs to look at. The head should be oval, almost egg-shaped, without stop. The profile should be almost an arc from the occiput to the nose-tip; the back short, strong and muscular, and the chest broad. Coat: short, flat and rather harsh to the touch. Colour: white or brindle. Height 20–22 in. Weight: 45–50 lb.

(The Miniature Bull Terrier should be a miniature of the above in every respect. Height: 12–14 in. Weight: not to exceed 20 lb.)

The Cairn Terrier. The name Cairn Terrier was, according to Ash,[1] first used in 1887. But the type (for at that date it certainly could not be called a breed) did not come into prominence until 1908, when Mrs. Alistair Campbell and the Marchioness of Aberdeen began to publicise them. Scotland is, of course, the home of many rough-haired, short-legged terriers, and it is impossible to say with certainty which was the original type. But it seems probable that it was the Cairn. The breed achieved great popularity between the wars, and their registrations annually still outnumber those of any other terrier breed. Essentially, the Cairn Terrier should be a game-working dog. There is a tendency nowadays to lessen the

[1] *Dogs: Their History and Development.*

size and to turn them into drawing-room pets, and it is to be hoped that this tendency will not be allowed to get out of hand. The head should be wedge-shaped, broad between the ears and with a definite stop, and the ears small and pointed. Body compact and of medium length. Tail short and carried gaily. Coat: profuse and hard with dense undercoat resembling fur. Colour: red, sandy, grey, brindle. Height: about 10 in. Weight: about 14 lb.

The Dandie Dinmont Terrier. Made famous by Sir Walter Scott in *Guy Mannering*, and the only dog to take its name from a literary source. The origin is as confused as that of all the other Scottish and Border breeds. 'Stonehenge' maintained that it was the result of crossing the Otterhound with a Scottish Terrier, which seems to be extremely unlikely. Dogs resembling the Dandie Dinmont, and known as 'Mustard-and-Pepper' terriers, were known along the Border in the eighteenth century, but the breed did not become well known in England until about 1875. By 1890 it had acquired the shape that we now know, which is certainly not the shape that Sir Walter Scott knew. However, the modern Dandie Dinmont retains a good deal of the old hard-bitten character and a refreshing eagerness for sport. The head is strongly made, large and broad between the ears. The body is long, strong and flexible, and the chest well let down between the forelegs. The hind-legs are a little longer than the forelegs. The tail is short. Coat: a mixture of hard and soft hairs and about 2 in. long. (The coat is known as pily.) Colour: pepper or mustard, the pepper varying from a dark blue-black to a light silver-grey, the mustard ranging from reddish-brown to pale fawn. Height: 8–11 in. Weight: about 18 lb.

The Fox Terrier (Smooth). A breed of comparatively recent origin, though the use of terriers for bolting foxes and badgers is very ancient. 'Stonehenge', writing in 1879, was contemptuous of the Fox Terrier, maintaining (even at that date) that 'not one per cent.' had ever come across the scent of a fox. He was also of the opinion that the Beagle had been used to produce the white strain of Smooth Fox Terrier. There is, as far as I know, no evidence to support this contention. The modern Smooth Fox Terrier, though resembling the Hunt terriers scarcely at all, is a well-formed, lively and thoroughly sporting dog; often a good ratter and capable (as I have seen) of following a fox down a train. (This particular dog, incidentally, was a household pet and a town dog that had never

Pomeranian.

King Charles Spaniel.

Chihuahua.

Yorkshire Terrier.

been entered to fox, and had probably never so much as smelt a rat.) That so much of the old instinct remains, and that the breed is still of so serviceable a shape, speaks volumes for the specialist association. The head is flat and moderately narrow, and the jaws strong and muscular. The neck is muscular, thickening towards the shoulders, which are well laid back, long and sloping. The chest is deep, the back short, strong and straight, and the hind-quarters very strong and muscular. Coat: straight, flat, smooth, hard, dense and abundant. Colour: white should predominate, marked with black or tan. Height: about 15 in. Weight: 15–18 lb.

The Fox Terrier (Wire). More recent in origin than the Smooth Fox Terrier, the Wire has far out-stripped its cousin in popularity. Their rise has been entirely in the present century, and during the last forty years they have been altered by the specialist breeders almost out of recognition. The Wire Fox Terrier is too well known to merit description. The modern 'cubist' shape is only a fashion. Trimming for exhibition has been legalised. There is now no point in discussing the ethics of the practice, but it may be said that clever manipulation has made many a poor dog look a great deal better. No doubt the competent judge is never deceived by trimming, but I would not like to say the same for the general public. Be that as it may, there can be no doubt that the Wire Fox Terrier makes an elegant and attractive pet for the modern urban householder, who has, after all, no need for a sporting dog, and is probably much better off without one. Coat: dense and wiry, the hairs having a tendency to twist. Colour: predominantly white with black or tan markings. Height: not more than 15½ in. Weight: about 18 lb.

The Griffon Bruxellois. A very ancient breed of the Low Countries, probably the ancestor of all the Scottish and northern rough-haired terriers. Though now a 'toy' breed, this is a comparatively recent development: until the middle of the nineteenth century the breed was much the same size as the Cairn Terrier. Though a 'toy', the Griffon Bruxellois has the true temperament of a working terrier, being active, fearless and eager. Introduced into England in 1894. The head is large and rounded, with a prominent chin and a slightly undershot jaw. The chest is broad and deep, the back short and strong, the shoulders well laid back. The hindquarters are particularly strong and muscular. Coat: harsh and wiry, free from curl. Colour: clear red, black or black-and-tan. Height: about

10 in. Weight: about 10 lb., 6–9 lb. is considered particularly desirable. (There is also a smooth variety.)

The Irish Terrier. The origin of this magnificent breed is unknown, but it may safely be said that it is not, as some enthusiasts maintain, indigenous to Ireland. It is still used as a working terrier in Ireland, but it has never, I think, been so used in England. The breed is famed for its great courage and absolute fearlessness, and makes one of the best watch-dogs in the world. Though gentle with humans (especially those it knows), it is apt to resent interference from other dogs, and has acquired a very considerable reputation as a fighter. To their masters they are capable of complete devotion, but it has to be admitted that their fighing reputation has brought about some decline in popularity. The head is long, the skull flat and rather narrow between the ears. The jaws are muscular and very powerful. The chest is deep and muscular, the back strong and straight, and the legs straight and well-boned. The breed is, fortunately, not subject to over-trimming. Coat: hard and wiry, straight and flat. Colour: whole colours—red, red-wheaten or yellow-red. Height: 18 in. Weight: 25–27 lb.

The Kerry Blue Terrier. The breed used to be known as the Blue Irish Terrier. Whether it is older than the Irish Terrier or not is a matter of opinion upon which there will never be agreement among Irishmen. In Ireland this is a working breed, and is sometimes used for herding cattle. Introduced to England in 1922. It, too, has acquired a tremendous reputation as a fighter. The show dog is subject to a good deal of trimming. Larger and heavier than the Irish Terrier. Coat: soft and silky, plentiful and wavy. Colour: any shade of blue, with or without black points. Height: about 19 in. Weight: 35–37 lb.

The Lakeland Terrier. A new breed, but the amalgamation of a number of types of Lake District terriers, each of ancient if unknown ancestry. Formerly there was a good deal of disagreement between the supporters of the various types, but since the formation of the Lakeland Terrier Association in 1921 there has been steady progress. The breed was officially recognised in 1928. Though a show dog in the south, the breed is very much a working dog in its homeland and, since it is expected to attack foxes rather than merely to bolt them, it is exceptionally powerful for its size and quite remarkably hardy. The head is moderately broad, the skull flat, the jaws powerful. The shoulders are well laid back, the back strong, moderately short and well-coupled. The hind-quarters are strong and muscular, and the thighs long and powerful. Coat: harsh, dense and weather-resisting with a good undercoat. Colour: black-and-tan, blue-and-tan, red, wheaten, red grizzle, black, blue or liver. Height: not more than 14½ in. Weight: 15–17 lb.

The Manchester Terrier. This breed is still sometimes referred to as the Black-and-tan terrier. But the old Black-and-tan Terrier was a broken-haired dog, the modern Manchester Terrier (which is undoubtedly a descendant) is smooth-haired. A very smart dog, with nice clean lines and a beautiful coat with the gloss of satin, the Manchester Terrier deserves to be much more popular than it is. They were popular enough at the beginning of the century, and it is difficult to understand why they lost ground. The head is long and narrow, flat in skull and wedge-shaped. The ears are small, triangular carried well above the top line of the head, and dropped, hanging close to the head. The chest is deep and narrow, and the body fairly short and curving upwards at the loins. The tail, not docked, should be thick at the root, taper to a point and be carried straight out. Coat: smooth, short and glossy. Colour: jet black with rich mahogany tan markings. Height: about 16 in. Weight: 17–18 lb.

The Norwich Terrier. Small terriers of a working kind have been known in Norfolk and Cambridgeshire for almost a century, but the exact origin of the Norwich Terrier is not known. There can be little doubt that a small Irish Terrier was used in crosses with one of the Scotch terriers. The breed was recognised in 1932, but is still very far from standardised, some having prick-ears (these were once known as Trumpington Terriers) and some drop-ears. The Norwich Terrier is affectionate, active and hardy, gets on well with other dogs, and deserves to be much more popular than it is. The head is broad between the ears with a well-defined stop. The body is compact, medium in length, with a strong, straight back. The legs are relatively short, but straight, well-boned and very strong. Coat: hard, wiry, straight, lying close to the body except on the neck and shoulders, where it forms almost a mane, especially in winter. Colour: red, red-wheaten, black-and-tan or brindle. Height: 10 in. Weight: 11–12 lb.

The Schnauzer. Sometimes considered not to be a terrier because of its use as a cattle-dog (but see Kerry Blue Terrier). A German breed, known in that country since the early seventeenth century, it was introduced in 1928, but has never become really popular despite its affectionate nature and very considerable intelligence. A strongly built, robust dog, it has a moderately long head, broad between the ears; a moderately broad, deep chest and a strong, straight back. The tail is docked. Coat: hard, dense and wiry. Colour: all pepper and salt colours, or black. But black-and-tan and black-and-silver also occur, though they are not considered very desirable. Height: 18–19 in. Weight: 35–40 lb.

(The Miniature Schnauzer is identical but smaller, the height being about 14 in.)

The Scottish Terrier. Once known as the Aberdeen Terrier, and still so-called by many people. The breed first became widely known about 1875. The dogs of those days were more like the modern Cairn, and the head was much shorter than the head of the modern dog. This lengthening of the head was taken to a ridiculous pitch just before the First World War, and resulted in a nervous strain which did the breed a lot of harm. Though the head might, perhaps, still be considered a little long, the nervous strain appears to have been lost. The legs are short, and the back short, straight and muscular. The hindquarters are exceptionally powerful for the size of the dog. Coat: harsh, dense and wiry, with a short, soft and dense undercoat. Height: 10–11 in. Weight: 19–23 lb.

The Sealyham Terrier. The breed takes its name from the village of Sealyham in Pembrokeshire. It was evolved by Captain John Tucker Edwardes in the middle of the last century, but it is not known what ingredients he used. What he wanted was a short-legged dog that would be dead game to fox or badger, and he succeeded in producing a breed that rapidly became famous throughout South Wales. It is all the more curious, therefore, that they were not exhibited at an English show until 1910. They were successful from that moment. The modern dog is, of course, a very different dog from the dog that came from South Wales in 1910, but the old keenness has not been entirely lost, thanks to the efforts of Sir Jocelyn Lucas and others. Sir Jocelyn Lucas, indeed, has a famous pack of hunting Sealyhams. The breed is too well known to warrant description. Coat: long, hard and wiry. Colour: white, or white with lemon, brown or badger pied markings on head and ears. Height: not more than 12 in. Weight: 18–20 lb.

The Skye Terrier. Originally a hard, tough little terrier, closely resembling the Cairn, and used for sport with fox, otter and badger. The modern dog is an ornamental rather than a sporting terrier. This may be considered a triumph for the specialist breeders, as undoubtedly it is (though one may question the wisdom of producing coats of such inordinate length), but the result has been a steady decline in the popularity of the breed. The modern Skye Terrier has a long head with powerful jaws, and an exceptionally long body on short legs, the total length being 41 in. Coat: undercoat short, close, soft and woolly; overcoat long—averaging 5½ in.—hard, straight and flat. Colour: dark or light blue or grey, or fawn with black points. Height: 10 in. Weight: 25–30 lb.

The Staffordshire Bull Terrier. The old original fighting Bull Terrier, which survived, largely as the companion of the working classes in the Midlands, after Mr. Hinks had started improving his white breed for show. The breed was recognised by the Kennel Club in 1935 and is regularly exhibited, and indeed seems to be outstripping the Bull Terrier in popularity, if the number of registrations is anything to go by. But the old characteristics have not been lost: the Staffordshire Bull Terrier, when roused, is still a holy terror. The head is short and broad, with a distinct stop and pronounced cheek muscles. The ears are half-pricked and not large. The neck is short, thick and muscular, and the body is close-coupled, wide in front, with a level top line and rather light in the loins. The legs are straight and well-boned, and the dog gives the impression of immense power. Coat: smooth, short and close. Colour: red, fawn, black, blue, any of these colours with white, or whole white. Height: 14–16 in. Weight: 28–38 lb.

The Welsh Terrier. The origin of this sterling breed is unknown, but it is not improbable that it is a descendant of the old broken-haired Black-and-tan Terrier. The breed has been carefully nurtured by the Welsh Terrier Club, and there is a sensible show standard. The dog itself is affectionate and loyal, less excitable than most terriers and an excellent watch-dog. The head is of natural length (indeed, none of the points have been exaggerated) with strong and muscular jaws; the body is compact with straight back and a good depth of chest; and the legs are straight with good bone and muscle. Coat: wiry, hard, close and abundant. Colour: black-and-tan or black grizzle and tan. Height: 15½ in. Weight: 20–21 lb.

The West Highland White Terrier. Cairn Terriers used occasionally to throw white puppies in their litters. These were disliked and usually destroyed. But at the beginning of the present century Colonel E. D. Malcolm decided to save white puppies and breed from them, and he is generally credited with founding the West Highland White Terrier. The new breed soon became extremely popular, and to keep pace with the demand there was much inbreeding, with the result that a highly nervous strain developed. This has now been eradicated, and this little dog is excellent, lively, unaggressive and deservedly very popular. Selective breeding has altered the appearance from that of the Cairn, although the family likeness remains, by shortening the back, increasing the width of the head and the length of leg. Coat: outercoat hard, about 2 in. long and free from curl; undercoat short, soft, close, resembling fur. Colour: pure white. Height: about 11 in. Weight: 14–18 lb.

The Yorkshire Terrier. Originally bred by miners as a ratter, the Yorkshire Terrier is now truly a 'toy', the smallest of the British Terriers and one of the smallest breeds in the world. Even so, there is a considerable difference between the show specimen and the ordinary (and rather bigger) household pet. One might almost say that there are two types. The reason for this is the wonderful coat of the show specimen, which could not possibly be kept by the average owner in anything like condition. However, it is the toy which we consider here. The head is small with a round skull, slightly flattened on top and a definite stop. The body is very compact, with a short, quite straight back. The carriage is neat and the dog should have an important air. Coat: moderately long and perfectly straight, silky in texture and glossy like silk. Colour: dark steel blue with the hair on the chest a rich bright tan. Height: 8 in. Weight: up to 7 lb.

There are, of course, many other breeds present in Great Britain in small numbers. Many, probably most, of these are classified in a separate register at the Kennel Club under the general heading 'Any Other Variety'. Among them are:

The Ormskirk Heeler. A Corgi-type dog, not uncommon in the Ormskirk district of Lancashire. Colour: usually black-and-tan. Height: about 13 in. Weight: about 30 lb.

The Glen of Imaal Terrier. A small working Terrier from Ireland. Colour: wheaten, blue-tan, blue brindle. Height: 14 in. Weight: about 30 lb.

The Soft-coated Wheaten Terrier. Another Irish breed with a soft wavy coat. Colour: wheaten. Height: 17 in. Weight: 35 lb.

The Sydney Silky Terrier. An Australian breed. Coat silken and long. Colour: slate blue, blue-tan, sandy-red. Height: 10 in. Weight: 10 lb.

Weimaraners. A German Pointer breed. Coat: short and smooth. Colour: silver-grey, mouse-grey. Sometimes known as the 'grey ghost'. Height: 23 in. Weight: 50 lb.

Maremma Sheepdogs. An Italian sheepdog. Coat: soft and close, medium in length. Colour: white. Height: about 25 in. Weight: about 70 lb.

The Bearded Collie. An ancient, but now rare, Scottish breed. Coat: long, hard, shaggy with pronounced beard. Colour: black-and-tan, tricolour. Height: about 22 in. Weight: about 60 lb.

The Husky. Many different varieties—Greenland, Iceland, Eskimo, Malamute. There is some variation in size and weight for the different varieties. A typical Spitz dog. Colour: usually grey, white or black-and-white. Height: 22–28 in. Weight: 65–110 lb.

Tibetan Spaniel. Rather like a Pekingese with longer legs. Coat: silky with good feathering. Colour: black, black-and-tan, red, fawn. Height: about 10 in. Weight: 5–12 lb.

Tibetan Terrier. Rather like a miniature Old English Sheepdog in appearance. Sometimes known as the Lhasa Terrier. Coat: long, profuse, straight, falling over eyes. Colour: white, cream, grey, smoke, black. Height: 14 in. Weight: 25 lb.

Lhasa Apso. Another Tibetan breed. Very shaggy haired. Colour: gold, honey, sandy, fawn. Height: about 10 in. Weight: about 15 lb.

Shih Tzu. A Chinese breed. The name is pronounced 'Sheed Zoo'. Coat: long and dense, falling over eyes. Colour: all colours. Height: about 11 in. Weight: 12–16 lb.

Leonberger. A German breed, developed from crosses between the St. Bernard and the Newfoundland. Coat: long and soft, with a good mane. Colour: fawn or grey. Height: about 27 in. Weight: about 100 lb.

Rottweiler. Originally a cattle-dog. Now much used on the Continent as a guide-dog and for police work. Of almost legendary intelligence. Coat: smooth, short and close. Colour: black-and-tan. Height: about 25 in. Weight: 100–112 lb.

The Portuguese Water-dog. The ancestor of the Poodle and the Irish Water Spaniel. Coat: long, hard in texture. Should be clipped from the ribs back, but the tip of the tail left free. Colour: black, brown, black-and-tan, black-and-white. Height: about 22 in. Weight: about 45 lb.

The Akita. A Japanese Spitz breed. A typical Spitz. Was used by the Japanese Army. Coat: harsh, with soft, thick undercoat. Colour: cream, fawn, grey, brindle, black, red, black-and-tan. Height: about 23 in. Height: 50–55 lb.

BIBLIOGRAPHY

ARKWRIGHT, WILLIAM: *The Pointer and his Predecessors* (London, 1902).

ASH, EDWARD C.: *Dogs: Their History and Development* (London, 1927).

—— *The Book of the Greyhound* (London, n.d.).

—— *The Cocker Spaniel* (London, 1935).

—— *The Cairn Terrier* (London, 1936).

BROUGH, E.: *The Bloodhound* (Bradford, 1902).

CLARKE, H. EDWARDS: *The Modern Greyhound* (London, n.d.)

COLLIER, V.: *Dogs of China and Japan* (London, 1921).

COOK, CHARLES: *The Dandie Dinmont* (Edinburgh, 1885).

DUNBAR, LADY: *The Chow Chow* (London, 1914).

EDWARDS, SYDENHAM: *Cynographia Britannica* (London, 1800).

FARROW, JAMES: *The Clumber Spaniel* (Bradford, 1912).

GILBEY, SIR WALTER: *Hounds in Old Days* (London, 1913).

HUBBARD, C. L. B.: *Dogs in Britain* (London, 1948).

——*Working Dogs of the World* (London, 1947).

—— *The Literature of British Dogs* (Ponterwyd, 1949).

JESSE, GEORGE R.: *Researches into the History of the British Dog* (London, 1866).

KELLEY, R. B.: *Sheep Dogs* (London, 1947).

LAVERACK, EDWARD: *The Setter* (London, 1872).

LEE, RAWDON B.: *A History and Description of the Modern Dogs of Great Britain and Ireland* (London, 1893).

LEIGHTON, ROBERT: *The New Book of the Dog* (London, 1907).

LLOYD, FREEMAN: *The Whippet* (London, 1894).

LYTTON, HON. MRS.: *Toy Dogs and their Ancestors* (London, 1911).

MEYRICK, JOHN : *House Dogs and Sporting Dogs* (London, 1861).
PEARCE, THOMAS : *The Dog* (London, 1872).
RICHARDSON, E. H. : *British War Dogs* (London, n.d.)
SHAW, VERO : *The Illustrated Book of the Dog* (London, 1879).
SMITH, A. CROXTON : *British Dogs at Work* (London, 1906).
—— *Everyman's Book of the Dog* (London, 1909).
—— *Greyhound Racing and Breeding* (London, n.d.).
—— *About Our Dogs* (London, n.d.).
—— *Dogs since 1900* (London, 1950).
SMITH, CHARLES HAMILTON : *Dogs* (Edinburgh, 1840).
SOMERFIELD, ELIZABETH : *The Popular Boxer* (London, 1955).
VESEY-FITZGERALD, B. (ed.) : *The Book of the Dog* (London, 1946).
WALSH, J. H. ('Stonehenge') : *The Greyhound* (London, 1853).
—— *Manual of Rural Sports* (London, 1855).
—— *The Dog in Health and Disease* (London, 1859).
—— *Dogs of the British Isles* (London, 1867).
YOUATT, WILLIAM : *The Dog* (London, 1845).

INDEX

INDEX